A Life Misspent

Suryakant Tripathi Nirala (1896–1961) is associated with the Chhayavaad movement in Hindi poetry in the first half of the twentieth-century. He was a prolific poet and essayist, who altered the landscape of Hindi letters by the range and intensity of his art. Some of his most important works are *Parimal, Anaamika, Gitika, Tulsidas, Sandhya Kakali, Chaturi Chamar* and *Ravindra Kavita Kaanan*.

Satti Khanna is Associate Professor at Duke University, USA, where he teaches Indian Cinema and Modern Hindi Literature. He interprets the lives and works of contemporary Indian writers to an international audience through a series of documentary films and translations. He has translated Vinod Kumar Shukla's novels *Naukar ki Kameez* (*The Servant's Shirt*, Penguin, 1999) and *Khilega to Dekhenge* (*Once It Flowers*, HarperCollins, 2014) and Mohan Rakesh's travelogue *Aakhiri Chattan Tak* (*To the Farthest Rock*, HarperCollins, 2015). He has also translated Shukla's novella for young adults, *Hari Ghas ki Chhappar Vaali Jhopdi Aur Bauna Pahadd*, to be published by HarperCollins later this year.

SURYAKANT TRIPATHI NIRALA

A Life Misspent

Translated from the Hindi by

SATTI KHANNA

HARPER**PERENNIAL**

An Imprint of HarperCollins *Publishers*

First published in India in 2016 by Harper Perennial
An imprint of HarperCollins *Publishers*
Building No 10, Tower A, 4th Floor, DLF Cyber City, Phase II,
Gurugram – 122002
www.harpercollins.co.in

1 2 3 4 5 6 7 8 9 10

P-ISBN: 978-93-5136-476-4
E-ISBN: 978-93-5136-477-1

Typeset in 11/14 Adobe Text Pro by
Jojy Philip, New Delhi 110 015

I could not find a worthy person among the eminences of Hindi letters to whom this book could be dedicated. Eminences who possessed individual qualities similar to Kulli's seemed inadequate in comparison to the sum of Kulli's character. Therefore, I am deferring the ceremony of dedication.

Nirala

Preface

Kulli Bhaat, who was formally known as Pandit Patvaridin Bhatt, was my friend. This little book provides an account of his life. It also happens to provide an account of my life, more openly perhaps than the orthodox would like. But genuine literary people enjoy novelty. They may forgive the inclusion of autobiography in my tale if the telling has quality. It is to those who are open to the quality of things that I am most devoted.

Kulli Bhaat was human in a way that other human beings will honour. When I spoke to Pandit Devidatta Shukla, editor of *Saraswati*, about Kulli, Pandit Shukla said Kulli was his older brother's friend. Let the reader understand by this statement that Pandit Shukla esteemed Kulli as he would his elder brother.

The tone of the book is comic. It would be good if people did not take offence at it and thereby reveal their inadequacy as readers.

Nirala

Lucknow
10.5.1939

One

For a long time I had been unable to fulfill the wish that I should write a biography. There was no suitable person to write about, no leader of men. I looked everywhere. I tackled histories of the great ones. Book after book enumerated their ideals. I read biographies written by the great ones themselves. It became clear to me why India is an enslaved nation. Our heroes compensate for their weaknesses with grand statements. The blaze of light around what they say hides how they live.

I read this somewhere. A filmgoer saw a film star scale the wall of a house in a movie. The viewer, too, caught in the grip of passion, raced up the wall to his lover's house. He fell off and broke his back. I was glad. Many poets accomplish great deeds pen in hand. They put their lives in danger. They scale the seventh heaven of literary mastery. They father socialist revolutions.

The poet Tulsidas wrote:

> 'If I list my faults the tale grows long,
> If hints will serve I can carry on.'

Tulsidas believed in a poetic style suitable for ordinary, thoughtful persons. He said nothing about flourishes suitable for heroes. Literary critics are quick to remind us that Tulsidas was no hero; he was an ordinary man. Be that as it may, we know that Tulsidas retained his manly virtues from the time he came of age to the time of his demise a century later.

The poet Bhagvati Charan said to me—and poet Ramnaresh Tripathi knows this to be based on the latest research—that Tulsidas died of heatstroke. What made it so hot for him? Was it the dancing girl Ratnavali? And was heat the cause of the pain in his left arm when he composed the *Hanuman Bahuk*[1]? I am weak on history, but I do know that Tulsidas was a man, not a hero. Whereas Emperor Akbar was a hero. He started the Din-i-Ilahi faith. He married a woman from each of the religions practised in his empire. He gathered a large following.

My great-great grandfather's great-great grandfather, Raja Birbal Tripathi, was a follower of Emperor Akbar. Birbal married his daughter into the Vajpeyi priestly clan. Since then the Vajpeyis too have become capable of greatness. Kanyakubja descendents like myself, of course, benefitted directly from grandfather tripled.

In any case, just when I was hunting for a worthy subject, Kulli Bhaat died.

---

[1] Tulsidas' book of prayers to Lord Hanuman.

Two

Kulli Bhaat was not a public figure whose image could be managed. Only one person would have understood Kulli Bhaat's true significance and that person is no longer alive. I am speaking of Gorky. But Gorky too paid more attention to the figure a person cut than the substance of a person's life. He was an ideologue, a debater. Is there anyone in the world of Hindi letters who can judge such things? I hear a loud 'No'.

I may write a biography of interest to the wide Hindi-speaking world, but Kulli Bhaat himself lived in the provinces. The district of Rae Bareli was all he knew of land. In his declining days, he did travel once to the town of Ayodhya like a sailor voyaging across seas. The rest of his life he spent in the area around his native town of Dalmau. Through Kulli Bhaat I understood how Kabir could stand looking at ditchwater and imagine the seven seas.

Kulli never met any celebrity whose fame could rub off on him. The exception was Pandit Devidatta Shukla, editor of *Saraswati*. I was the one who informed Kulli that the man he knew was a famous editor. By then Kulli had only six months left to live.

'We were friends in elementary school,' Kulli said. 'Really, is he somebody important?'

I smiled. 'Your friend from elementary school edits the periodical Pandit Mahavir Prasad Dwivedi used to edit.'

Kulli seemed sceptical; he must have been a lot bigger than his friend in elementary school. Besides, Kulli was the one who introduced Shuklaji to Baiswari poetry. The relationship between them would have been Kulli guru and Shuklaji disciple. It was Kulli who had introduced me to Baiswari poets as well, to Narhari, Harinath, Thakur, Bhuvan and many others. I was overwhelmed by their poetic power. How could I count myself a poet compared to them? Kulli may not have known how low I ranked myself. To give him some sense of Shuklaji's stature I said, 'You think highly of me, but I am not fit to lace Shuklaji's shoes.'

Kulli was pleased at my words. He began to speak as an elder brother might or as Shuklaji himself might speak. 'Practice makes perfect. Which year was it when you came to take your wife home for the first time?' A look of timidity crossed his face, whose meaning I could not understand then, but which came to me in a flash now. Images of my first meeting with Kulli twenty-five years ago passed before my eyes. Let me begin with that first meeting.

Three

I had crossed the age of sixteen, as good as reached the end of my life according to J. P. Shrivastava. Not J. P. Shrivastava alone, but all our neighbours in the village thought the same. I remember Pandit Ramgulam speaking to my father: 'His voice has cracked. There's moustache on his lip. Hair has sprouted under his armpits. It's time to perform the bride-fetching ceremony and bring his wife home. Gets into fights, too, I hear.'

'Yes,' my father said and lapsed into thought.

In the same way, when we went to fetch my bride—she was thirteen—there was a puja going on knotting us together symbolically—I don't think it was a puja to the god of love— her grandmother said to her mother, 'Our daughter is of age. The son-in-law is of age. If they have come to take her away, let her go.'

So we brought my bride home.

But the plague was raging in our village. What were we to do? The custom was to abandon one's house during the plague and encamp in orchards. The day we travelled from Bengal was the day villagers were abandoning their houses. Before we left for my in-laws', my father had two bamboo huts constructed under a mahua tree in our orchard.

It was the month of June. I had never encountered Uttar Pradesh's scorching summer before. When we reached our village we were assigned one of the two huts. The door was shut upon us. Things I had never dreamed of became natural at the mere touch of my wife. I can assure young people that no maturing—not even what greybeards acquire over decades—goes as deep as this maturing.

On the fifth day, my father-in-law came to take his daughter back for the ceremonial return to her house. He did not want to drink water from our wells and he wanted to leave before nightfall. My father was offended. My father had not travelled from Bengal[2] to welcome the bride to our ancestral village for a paltry five days. He expected the daughter-in-law to stay longer. Father-in-law arrived in the morning. I had been up late the previous night and was asleep at the time. I heard about his visit from a friend in the village. By the time I awoke, Father-in-law had left with my wife. He didn't want her exposed to the plague.

Father was livid. 'Weren't you worried about my son being exposed? If this is how much you care, we can find a new bride for our son.' Father's threat might have had its desired effect if Father-in-law had not been hard of hearing. Father-in-law kept up a parallel flow of muttering of his own while he oversaw preparations for his departure. But Father-in-law's daughter was all ears. One can guess how the talk between her father and father-in-law about a second bride might have struck her. The ox-cart was summoned for the trip to the railway station. My father bade them a brusque goodbye.

[2] Mahishadal in Bengal where Nirala's father was employed as a security guard.

The barber from Dalmau came the next day, bearing a lengthy letter from Father-in-law. The word 'apology' was sprinkled liberally over its pages. Father-in-law's hearing was going. He had been unable to ascertain Father's wishes. He invited us to come and fetch the bride for the gavani move to her husband's home. Pleading. Pleading. And then the matter of a second marriage for me mentioned within hearing of a girl whose permanent teeth hadn't all come in.

Father softened. 'You can go to your in-laws,' he said to me. 'But make sure you eat three times as much as you eat here.'

'I will ask for three times the usual quantity of ghee and almonds. I would ask for pomegranate juice every morning if pomegranates grew there.'

'Insist on a perfume oil massage every day. That should stagger them back to their senses.'

I began preparations for the four o'clock train. The servant was sent ahead with a bedroll and a trunk. I followed him at two-thirty, fully apprised of my father's view of my in-laws. I had dressed in the Bengali style—dhoti, shirt, shoes, umbrella. I thought of every place except Bengal as wild forest or barren desert. I believed like Bengalis that Aryans became civilized when they crossed into Bengal, and really civilized when they came into contact with the British.

It had been cool in our water-sprinkled hut under the mahua tree. Ten steps outside the hut and Uttar Pradesh's summer wind hit me with the force of a blow. My kundalini came awake. It was, as the poet Rabindranath Tagore says of goddess Saraswati: she parted all the veils with a single flourish. The difference is that Tagore had the veils parted sitting in his easy chair, the Prophet Moses standing on top of a mountain, and my humble self jumping over a trench dug between the orchard and the main road. 'Go back,' the winds of reality said to me. 'Now that you have gained true knowledge, return to your hut.'

My steps did not turn homeward. The courage I had imbibed from Bengal was backed by the power of love. I stumbled into a ditch as I marched ahead. I was lucky that a wild plum bush growing there broke my fall. I picked myself up smeared with Uttar Pradesh dirt and plum juice; I no longer looked the Bengali gentleman. But praise to the poet Surdas! I could find a frame of reference for my misfortune. I had only recently seen the Bilvamangal play in Calcutta. Bilvamangal rode a corpse across a river thinking it a raft. He climbed up a live snake to the balcony of his beloved thinking it a rope. Bilvamangal pursued a mere courtesan while I was travelling to rejoin my newly wedded wife. I remained resolute. Another gust of UP air assailed me. It's not the earth that scorches; it's the air. Kalidasa's line sprang to mind: *'Vanquish the earth by force of will'*. Onward. My shoe waged its own battle with a stone on the footpath. The stone pried its jaw open. Never mind, I thought. I have a spare pair in my bag. Another gust. The umbrella turned inside out. I had to spin around to right the umbrella.

The Lon river came into view, dry eight months of the year and choked with thorny bushes. The region used to be called Forest-killer, probably from all the plum and babool bushes which overran it. And yet there were twelve principalities carved out of this tiny region, twelve different princes seeking independence for their locality. I had on a dhoti with a multicoloured border. The border flew up to embrace a thorn bush and refused to be parted. A hundred thorns poked through the dhoti. I was getting late. A hard tug at the edge of the cloth and the dhoti filled with gashes. Triangular victory pennants fluttered on the thorn bush.

It had been an expensive dhoti, woven in Shantipur and purchased expressly for the first visit to my in-laws the way writers write essays expressly for particular magazines. I took comfort from the thought of other dhotis packed in my bag.

I climbed out of the riverbed. The Behta cremation ground lay ahead. I heard the growling of an engine. A mile of barren ground stretched between me and the train station. I broke into a run. 'It is unbecoming to run,' I scolded myself. Umbrella tucked under my arm, shoes in hand, mid-afternoon heat overhead. I could see the station. The engine was taking water. I quickened my pace. The sand beneath my feet burned like coals. Faster. My clothes clung to my body. Any second now I would stumble and break my neck.

Our servant, Chandrika Prasad, the one whose permanent teeth never grew out, chose this moment to raise his head and look in my direction. His lips sat unevenly over the hollow mouth. He had already bought train tickets. I was filled with hope. He smiled on seeing me, handed me my ticket and pushed the luggage in from the side of the station where there was no railway platform. There was only one platform at the station. Chandrika had gotten off it wondering where I was. Now he helped us get in from the wrong side.

The interior of the carriage was hot as an oven. If Chandrika had not fanned me with his shoulder cloth I would have passed out. It grew cooler once the train began to move. I put on fresh clothes.

Dalmau was the fifth stop. The sun was low on the horizon, but there was enough light to make out faces. Chandrika picked up our luggage and walked past the ticket-checker. There was a man standing by the gate, dressed in the Lucknow style—hair slicked down, curls, Nehru cap askew. A Bengali would have glanced at his kurta, his black-bordered dhoti, his fine shoes from Meerut and typed him immediately as a small town crook. Whether Muslim or Hindu hard to tell. Age twenty-five, give or take a couple of years. To the ordinary eye, tall and well-built.

He approached as soon as I had surrendered my ticket. 'Which way are you headed?'

'Sherandazpur,' I said.

'Come with me. I have my trap here.' He called out to the driver while inspecting me carefully. 'Where are you staying?'

I gave my father-in-law's name. I took no special notice of the man. I had judged quickly that the man's shape and build did not match my ideal. He was two inches shorter than me and lighter of build.

I sat in front with the driver of the trap. Chandrika sat by me. The master of the trap gazed at me for some time before taking his seat in the back. I did not recognize the gaze then; I do now. It is the sort of gaze bestowed upon an exceedingly beautiful woman at the height of her beauty.

Chandrika stared idiotically first at him, then at me. The master of the trap was silent, lost in his emotions. I had nothing to say. The trap moved forward, entered the quarter where my father-in-law lived and stopped in front of his house. The master had jumped off at the street crossing. I didn't think he had spoken to the driver before he got off.

When I began to count out the fare, the driver said his master had instructed him not to accept payment. 'I know nothing about your master. He is not my master in any case. If he didn't want to be paid he should have told me so at the outset.'

The driver put out his hand, but added, 'I will lose my job if he finds out.' I realized he would pocket the fare. By now many people from my in-laws' house came out to the trap. I got ready to greet them.

Four

I bent down and touched my mother-in-law's feet. She pointed me to a bed on which a galeecha had been laid. When I looked up I saw anxiety written on her face. 'Was it Kulli's trap you travelled on from the station?'

Kulli must be an untouchable. 'Such scruples are outdated now,' I said. But Mother-in-law's anxiety did not disappear. She kept glancing at my long, wavy hair combed in the Bengali way. Had she made an unnatural choice for her daughter? Would her child's life be ruined forever? The printed border of my dhoti seemed to confirm her suspicions. She heaved a sigh and went into the inner rooms.

From where I sat, I could see a chilval tree in the courtyard. That must be the branch from which they hang a swing, I thought to myself. The girl who swings on that swing singing ragas of the rainy season must be singing about me—about the pangs of separation and the joy of union.

A young woman's laughter rippled out from an inner room. I had not heard this particular laugh before, but I had no trouble recognizing whose it was. Its waves carried deep meaning for me. They said, 'You are mine, I know it. Having you, I lack nothing. Others may not recognize who you are. I recognize you and I am content.'

Chandrika was sitting on a bedroll staring at the sky. The stars were out. 'Tell me,' he said, 'Are there more people on earth or more stars in the sky?'

'What is your view?' I asked.

Chandrika smiled, 'Who says the earth is smaller than the sky, horizon to horizon, end to end? There are more people.'

Mother-in-law brought lemonade. Their servant had just stepped out. When he returned she asked him to serve water. Her face was radiant, brighter than the bright moon. Her daughter must have dispelled the doubts in her mind. She said to me in an affectionate tone, 'Here, son, drink your lemonade.'

I sipped the beverage. Mother-in-law sighed again, a long sigh of relief. Chandrika finished his glass of lemonade.

Mother-in-law tossed a blanket on the floor and sat upon it. Once she was settled, she proceeded to criticize my father, describing him as a heartless barbarian. I had half a mind to tell Mother-in-law about her own barbarity, but I remembered I was here to build a mood for love. Rough conduct was out of place. Her daughter was a jewel, Mother-in-law said, accomplished in letters and music. If my father abandoned a bride like her and married me elsewhere, the worst possible karma would accrue to me.

I held my peace. Mother-in-law concluded I was worthy of trust. 'I married her to you for your handsomeness, not for the folds of prosperity on your father's belly.' I concluded she wanted me to be loyal to her, against my father's wishes if necessary. 'Tell me,' she asked confidentially, 'is my daughter a beauty or not?'

I have never fared badly in oral interviews. 'It is true I have touched your daughter,' I said, 'and I have spoken to her as well, but I haven't had a good look at her. When it was my time to be with her the lamps were put out. I took a matchbox in with me the next night. I had scarcely lighted the match when your daughter turned her face away; neighbours in nearby huts began to cough. I didn't have the courage to light a second match.'

Mother-in-law smiled at this and returned to the inner rooms.

I noticed that Mother-in-law had given me full marks just as Raibahadur Pandit Shukdev Vihari Mishra gave a hundred out of a hundred to the poet Sumitranandan Pant. That is to say, a large kerosene lamp was placed in our bedchamber at night, so that I might enjoy full sight of her daughter's beauty.

I lay down in delicious anticipation. With footsteps sweeter than any musical meter, the daughter entered our room and handed me a fold of paan. 'Is it true,' she asked, 'that you travelled to our house on Kulli's trap?'

Who is this Kulli? What is this trap? I tried to solve the mystery while my bride stood before me, smiling at my bafflement.

Five

I woke up late. Mother-in-law came in to ask if I needed anything for my toilet. I washed quickly and sat down to read. Mother-in-law reported that Kulli had come by at daybreak. She had told him I was sleeping—he should return later in the day. 'But it's not nice to spend time with people like Kulli,' she added.

'If he has come all the way to the house it isn't proper to refuse to see him.'

'He is not a good man,' Mother-in-law said gravely.

'But he is a man, and therefore...'

'I didn't say he was a creature with horns. Only among men do we distinguish those who are good from those who are not.'

'If you are so confident of your judgment why didn't you tell him to stay away?'

'As our son-in-law, you are the guest of the entire town. Anyone from the town who wants to can come and visit. It would be discourteous of me to prevent them from coming to see you.'

'Should I be the person, then, to refuse to see someone who is eager to meet me?'

'That is not what I meant. If you associate with him people may think poorly of you.'

'On the other hand, if he associates with me people may begin to think well of him.'

Mother-in-law scanned my face for symptoms of my contagious goodness.

Kulli returned just then. He asked for me in a stage whisper, 'Is he awake yet?'

Mother-in-law frowned. My wife crossed the courtyard rapidly. From the first I have been one to choose the direct route of confrontation. Why should Kulli be dangerous? I must go and meet him. When I came out, he joined his palms in greeting as if we were old friends. I liked the welcome and returned his greeting.

During the day, I had my spot in the sitting area. A bed with a fresh cover would be laid out for me. A cot made of twine stretched over a wood frame lay nearby. Kulli sat on the cot to indicate that the superior seat on the bed was intended for me.

A tray of paan arrived. Kulli took the tray from the servant and respectfully offered it to me. I took two folds for myself and asked Kulli to have some, too. Kulli smiled, picked up two folds of paan and laid the tray at one end of the cot.

Our conversation turned to the history of the town. 'Dalmau belonged to Dal Baba,' Kulli Bhaat said. 'He built a fort for himself.' While Kulli spoke, he looked at me in a peculiar manner, as if I was related to him in some way. I was puzzled, but I enjoyed the attention.

'Can the fort still be seen?'

'Its ruins can be. The peasants say the fort collapsed because Dal Baba laid a curse on it. There was a battle with the Shah of Jaunpur. Soldiers from Dalmau and Bareli joined together to fight against the Shah. We hold an annual fair at the battle site. The Shah won and Muslims gained control of the fort and its environs. The Shah's summer house is at Makanpur. His grave is in Dalmau. Earlier the region belonged to Kannauj. Jaichand's campsite is nearby, just beyond the Chaurasi.'

I was thrilled that our Father in the Sky had situated my in-laws in such a historic town. My wife was a daughter of this soil. I was linked to the land through her. Therefore, I was significant. I looked at the provider of this information with gratitude.

Kulli added that there were a number of bathing ghats along the river worth visiting. Raja Tikatrai's embankment provided a fine view. There was a monastery above the river and an abandoned village adjacent to it.

'I shall see them all,' I said.

'I will be happy to come along,' Kulli responded. 'The sun is high now. How about this afternoon at four?'

'That will be good,' I said.

'There is a strong tradition of poetry in our region,' Kulli went on to say. 'My own ancestors have been renowned for their skill.' He mentioned the names of a number of poet-ancestors. I paid careful attention and committed these names to memory. Kulli left soon after, his eyes continuing to regard me with rapt fascination.

How strange the world is. This is the remarkable man whom my in-laws view with dark suspicion.

Mother-in-law saw that I was alone. She had peeked in a dozen times while Kulli was present. 'Is Kulli gone?'

'He seems to be a person of substance judging from his conversation.'

'Have you read the Ramayana?' Mother-in-law asked.

'Even though I am not a girl who has read the Ramayana to appear educated to her husband-to-be, I do know a few things about the text. If you are bent on examining me I can tell you that Kulli is no Ravana or Kumbhakarna.'

Mother-in-law smiled. 'In spite of your superior airs you have failed the test. I wasn't thinking of Ravana or Kumbhakarna, but you can recall, if you wish, the episode in which Ravana dresses up like a yogi to abduct Sita. The demon I had in mind was Kalanemi.'

'The one about whom Tulsidas says, "Kalanemi like a darker Ravana..."?'

'I believe you when you say you have read the Ramayana, but the allusion is to...' Mother-in-law was smiling.

'Is it the Hanuman episode where he catches hold of the feet and smashes them down?'

'A wonderful allusion, but you mustn't be quick. I was recalling how even Lord Shiva could not see through the deceit of Kalanemi speaking to him as a well-educated Brahmin.'

'I didn't think of that. But you could have told your daughter to whisper the secret of the disguise the way the crocodile houri warned her husband.'

'My daughter is no crocodile, nor has she seized you like one. She does not need to appear to you in her houri form. If you kill her to get to her secret, the sin will be upon your head.'

I was impressed by Mother-in-law's knowledge of mythology, especially impressed because I could not understand her.

She seated herself on the cot which Kulli had occupied recently. 'So what did you and Kulli talk about?'

I relaxed. I mentioned Kulli's attractive account of the history of Dalmau.

'I was right about Kalanemi,' Mother-in-law remarked.

'Why do you say that? Is there no fort in Dalmau?'

'There is,' Mother-in-law responded. 'I don't think that is the fort he wants you to visit.'

'How do you know?'

'He's cunning. Be sure to take Chandrika with you when you go.'

'Why? Will it take two of us to overcome one of him?'

Mother-in-law smiled again. 'Parents can't give children an explanation for everything. Go bathe. Dinner will be ready soon.'

Six

From childhood on I was a lover of freedom. I couldn't bear restrictions when they lacked all reason. An example may not be out of place. I had turned eight. Father came back to the village for my sacred thread ceremony. Pandit Bhagwan Deen Dubey was a landowner and revenue collector for the village. He kept a mistress and had four children by her, one daughter and three sons. I am talking about a time after Pandit Bhagwan Deen had passed away. Talluka was the name of the son he had by his wife. Because Bhagwan Deen died suddenly, he was unable to assign a portion of the property to his second family.

The children by the mistress complained at revenue collection time; they asked for their share of the proceeds. To pacify them, the legitimate son transferred some lands to them, enough to keep them comfortable. The mistress was in good health. Her sons were named Shamsher Bahadur, Jang Bahadur and Fateh Bahadur. The daughter was named Paraga.

Fateh Bahadur was the youngest illegitimate son, eight years older than me. The eldest brother had been educated with great care by Pandit Bhagwan Deen. Later in life, I heard a sitar recital by him. His precise phrasing of the music is stamped in my memory. I have heard that Pandit Bhagwan Deen organized a sacred thread ceremony for Shamsher Bahadur. He used his standing as a revenue officer to coerce many Brahmins into attending the sacred thread feast. He also arranged a proper Hindu wedding for Shamsher. The bride was not a Brahmin, but she was a Brahmin's widow. She had been married into a Brahmin family. From the time of Shamsher's wedding, the sons considered themselves Brahmin. Whenever it was advantageous to do so, they signed themselves with the Brahmin family name of Dubey. They treated their mother as Hindus treat foreigners, eating separately from her and sending her food in special containers not to be mixed with their own pots and pans.

These aspirations to purity notwithstanding, people of the village disowned them the moment Pandit Bhagwan Deen died. No one in the village invited them to feasts and ceremonies; no one in the village came to share a meal with them in their home.

This is how things stood at the time I returned to the village. As an act of revenge, the illegitimate sons had learned by heart the secret history of every family. Anyone who talked to them in a friendly manner was treated to a detailed account of these secrets—Ramcharan's widowed daughter became pregnant by Lakhu Pasi. Shiv Prasad Misir's twenty-year-old daughter, impatient at having remained unmarried, ran away with Lachman Lodh. Ram Dulare Tiwari was involved with his younger brother's widow. While Sundar Singh's son served in the army, Sundar Singh carried on with his daughter-in-law. Word got around that she was pregnant.

Sundar Singh paid off the police who came to inquire. He told the villagers he was escorting the daughter-in-law to her husband's army post but travelled with her to Calcutta instead. A boy was born to his daughter-in-law. Sundar Singh murdered the baby and escorted the daughter-in-law to his son's unit. He told his son that he had taken the daughter-in-law to Calcutta for treatment of diarrhoea.

Pandit Bhagwan Deen's 'natural' family influenced me the most. The sons of the family were impressive—in their physique, in their way of talking, in the grace and agility of their movements. Since my sacred thread ceremony had not yet been performed, I had a child's freedom to come and go anywhere I pleased. Their mother treated me with affection. She would feed me snacks and tell me entertaining stories. She also taught me a few ghazals and light ragas which were popular at the time.

One day the youngest son, the one who was my ideal, told me that my uncle used to be in the employ of his family. 'Our horse champed his hand off, rendering him useless for heavy labour. We gave him some land by way of compensation. These are the fields your aunt cultivates today.'

The story is true but the chronology inaccurate. When Pandit Bhagwan Deen gifted land to my uncle, Bhagwan Deen's 'natural' progeny had not been born. At the time I did not know the natural family had played no part in the transfer of land. I felt indebted to the natural family for their solicitude.

'Right now you're happy to eat what's cooked in our kitchen,' Fateh Bahadur said. 'Once your sacred thread ceremony is performed, you will not eat with us any more.'

'That's not fair,' I thought to myself. 'If I can eat with the natural family today why can't I eat with them after my sacred thread ceremony?'

Paraga, whom I treated like a sister, said to me, 'You will eat mahua gruel from Badloo Sukul's kitchen, but you will not touch halwah from ours.'

I was embarrassed. I would never choose gruel over halwah.

The sacred thread ceremony took place a few days later. By then each member of Pandit Bhagwan Deen's natural family had prepared me to rebel. I vowed to myself that I would continue eating with them as before. Their argument made sense. How could people in the village eat with them a few years earlier and not eat with them now?

My father took me aside the day after the ceremony. 'Don't eat food cooked by the prostitute.'

'Her sons don't eat food cooked by her,' I countered. 'They have other cooks.' If Father had explained things patiently I might have heeded him. But he bellowed at me: 'Don't eat food touched by them.'

'Did you eat food touched by them when their father was revenue collector?'

Father bit his lip. 'Do as I say.'

My heart would not accept what Father had instructed me to do. For two or three days after the ceremony, I stayed close to the house, putting on my sacred thread and taking it off. When neighbours noticed that I had not gone to the house of Pandit Bhagwan Deen's mistress they understood that I had come around. Father had prevailed.

It was the third or fourth day after my sacred thread

ceremony. I saw Fateh Bahadur at the village well. He was getting ready to bathe, drawing a bucket of water for the purpose. He smiled when he saw me approaching. The smile stabbed me like a dagger. I mastered my shame at the implied reproach and went up to him. 'Bhaiya, can you pour me water to drink?'

Fateh Bahadur felt proud. He poured water from the bucket into a lota and offered it to me. My taking a drink of water poured by him confirmed his Brahminical purity to the rest of the villagers. To me the drink confirmed fulfillment of the promise I had made to Fateh Bahadur's family.

The passers-by before whom Fateh Bahadur paraded his status were not to be defeated so easily. They took the case to my father. 'In front of the entire village,' the elders told him, 'your son has just drunk water from a lota poured by the youngest son of the prostitute. Your son is young and ignorant; we forgive him this time. But if he maintains contact with the prostitute's family, we will have no choice about breaking off relations with you.'

The delegation of local Brahmins presented their case politely. Father was a security guard in excellent health. I had violated explicit instructions. His caste-identity was in danger. As the saying goes, 'No shame so great as excommunication from your caste.' Father began to beat me with vigour worthy of his security guard training. He quite forgot that I was his only begotten son, the offspring of the second of two marriages. I bore the beating. I was obstinate by nature and I had learned endurance from the numerous beatings I received from early childhood on.

While Father's hands struck me quick as lightning, and

I cried from the blows, I also remembered scenes from earlier beatings. Once during a bitter winter, I had shat in a bush near the house instead of going to an open field, and I had wiped myself in the European style using aubergine leaves for toilet paper. I was about to step into the kitchen for dinner when a female relative who had spied my hasty improvization told Father how unclean I was. He caught hold of my foot and carried me dangling by it all the way to the village pond. He dunked me in the pond saying out loud: 'This is the way to wash up when you are done with shitting.' After a sufficient number of dunkings in cold water, he decided to generate compensating heat by slapping me in the face.

Another time I had taken Father aside. 'You are jamadar over so many guardsmen. Why don't you march with them and loot the Raja's treasury?' Father thought an enemy had put me up to making the suggestion so Father might lose his job. 'Whose idea is this?' Father thundered at me while raining blows. What could I say? The idea had been my own. The more I took responsibility for the idea the more Father smelled a conspiracy. At some stage in the proceedings, I passed out. (From that time to this—I am now forty-two years old—I have not forgotten what insecure employment can drive a man to.)

With each new slap, Father asked me to promise I would never visit the prostitute or her children again. I promised. The beating stopped.

The bruises healed and I went out again. As ill luck would have it, the situation that led to the beating repeated itself. The leader of the local Brahmins appeared at our door fuming with righteousness. 'Are you determined to destroy the Hindu dharma?' the leader shouted. 'We saw your son share roasted chickpeas with the prostitute's son. Beginning now, you and your family are barred from contact with any Brahmin family in the town.'

My father had the stronger personality. There was also the matter of the leader raising his voice. 'Don't you make your money selling toddy? And doesn't your daughter make hers turning tricks in Patna City? I have seen her at it. Chaudhury Bhagwan Deen may have been immoral. Why didn't you say that to his face? You were busy currying favour in those days, helping with toilet training for his sons. You're a fine one to bar us from anything!'

The spittle dried in the leader's throat. He looked ill as he left.

Father called out after him, grave and affectionate: 'Leader! Here, chew a little of our tobacco before you go.'

'I am a mature person. They are trying to confuse me. I will judge Kulli for myself. If Chandrika is forced on me as an escort, it will be easy enough to distract him. I will send him on an errand, to get body oil for massage. 'Wait for me at the crossroads when you return with the body oil.' I need a little time alone with Kulli to understand why there is so much suspicion of him.' I was thinking these thoughts when there was a rapping on the door. 'May I enter?' The voice was soft. Cultured. I understood it must be Kulli's.

'Please come in,' I said with matching courteousness. He was an hour early, hair freshly oiled, a waistcoat over his muslin kurta, a cane, socks even in the heat of summer. A pale-faced supplicant. I remembered a line from Kalidasa

for no reason: '*Small talk from the lover like cooling breezes.*'
I was not averse to flattery then. I did not understand its
hidden meaning. Nor did I have Kalidasa's knowledge of
sexual matters. Had I been wiser I would have dismissed
Kulli instantly.

I accepted the cardamom Kulli offered me for sweetening
the breath. 'You are an hour early,' I said.

'I thought we might want to visit Pandeyji's temple on
the way.'

Mother-in-law had been wary from the first. She had her
bed pulled into the verandah. She asked Chandrika to take
his afternoon nap on the verandah as well, plying him with
questions about how we lived, what we ate, what kind of
people we were.

Chandrika was a blabbermouth. You could get the darkest
family secret out of him in no time. He appeared in my
room in a little while dressed to go out, hair well-groomed,
walking staff in hand.

Kulli seemed surprised to see Chandrika with me. He
asked Chandrika for a jug of water and, while Chandrika
was away, Kulli turned to me. 'Is he coming along? What do
we want him for?'

Kulli's questions piqued my curiosity. 'Accompanying
me is part of his job, but I can always send him away on an
errand.' Kulli understood this in his own way. He imagined
that I knew what he desired and would arrange things
accordingly. I was the man he took me for.

Kulli accepted the jug of water Chandrika brought
him. 'The heat is terrible, splits one's head open,' he said.
Meanwhile Chandrika was estimating whether he could

bring Kulli down with one blow. Kulli splashed some water on his face, then drank a few sips. 'Let's not waste more time,' he said.

I went inside. Mother-in-law stood rigid at the door and my wife right behind her. I went straight to my room, put on fresh clothes and shoes and ran a comb through my hair. I picked up my umbrella and stepped outside. Mother-in-law blocked my way. She handed me a peasant staff and said I should take it along. 'The path goes through the forest,' she said.

'I can use the umbrella if there's danger,' I replied.

My wife smiled.

Kulli was waiting by the door to keep me from turning back once I had set out. He walked behind me, followed by Chandrika. Kulli glanced back at Chandrika with contempt but said nothing. I stopped when Kulli stopped on the road. Chandrika stopped as well. Kulli couldn't hide his irritation. I remembered Mother-in-law telling me that Kulli was less interested in the fort than in getting me away from the house. I was curious to know what Kulli was after. When we reached the main road Kulli signalled that I should dismiss Chandrika. I enjoyed the way Kulli turned up his mouth and arched his eyebrows when doing so. He looked crestfallen when I did not motion Chandrika away. Kulli's pace slackened, but he didn't lose hope. We continued in this manner towards the Shiva temple.

At the temple we received darshan of the deity and looked at frescoes. We wanted to rest too, and listen to the priest's conversation. Kulli was beside himself with impatience. The priest told us that the deity's birthday that year fell on the same day as Muharram. The Shia carried paper shrines mourning the deaths of Hasan and Hussain. Inside the temple, the priest waved arti lamps to the accompaniment of loud music. The temple festivities were not out of place, the priest told the police inspector who came to inquire. The Muslims were mourning martyrs whose remains had never been found while the Hindus celebrated the birth of God himself. (I heard a son had been born to the priest the same day).

Kulli interrupted to ask leave of the priest. 'We have many other things to see,' Kulli said. Ignoring numerous signals from Kulli that we should be going, I got up only when the priest had finished his story. Kulli continued to communicate by signs as we left the temple precincts, a fact that did not escape Chandrika's notice. Chandrika had imagined he would be needed to beat Kulli to a pulp, but he discerned something gentle in Kulli's communication with me. He was mystified.

I chose this moment to send Chandrika to buy perfumed massage oil from the perfume maker. He was in a fix. Mother-in-law had told him not to let me out of sight. 'The friend may turn out to be an enemy.' But Kulli didn't fit the description of an enemy. Chandrika said weakly, 'I would have enjoyed seeing more of the fort.'

'Will the fort be closed from now on? You can see it tomorrow if you wish. Do as your master says. Go and buy the perfumed oil. The shop is just ahead,' Kulli added.

Chandrika looked to me for guidance.

I said in an excited voice, 'Wait for us by this lane or on the main road. We should be back within the hour.'

Chandrika turned to leave. Kulli puffed his chest out in victory. I enjoyed watching him. We lacked such charming mannerisms in Bengal.

The fort began to be visible as we descended a slope. There were two mounds adjacent to one another. The building stood on top of the mounds. It appeared that the entire area of the fort had been walled in brick. Some of the bricks were large. Others were thin like our Lucknow bricks but more durable. We came to a wonderful gate built of these slender bricks. The path to the gate rose up like the ascent to a drinking pool for farm animals. It was also paved with fine bricks. We walked through the gate into the fort. A kind of intoxication comes over one in ancient places. Kulli pointed to the mound across from us. 'Those are the queen's quarters,' he said. 'We can make them out even though the building has settled. The gallery can be seen lower down. There is a cellar, too, with hidden treasure, people say.'

We went forward. The ruins of a mosque lay before us. 'The mosque was built after the Shah had conquered the town. It seems new in comparison to the other buildings. Up ahead is where soldiers were quartered; all that remains is these graves. A succession of gates led from here to the summerhouse. There were sentry stations and soldiers on duty. Notice how the land climbs and how high it gets by the summerhouse,' Kulli said.

He pointed out a well that had gone dry. Bordering it was the fort's sewage ditch where Hindu statues had been tossed when Muslims conquered the fort. A heap of statues could still be seen in there. 'There was said to be a tunnel leading from the ditch to the outside.'

We continued towards the summerhouse. 'This used to be a beautiful structure,' Kulli said. 'The British repaired it and turned it into a court building.'

I stood on a hilltop. The Ganga flowed below. Some stones among the ruins indicated a flight of steps that must have led from the summerhouse down to the water. The Ganga was wide here. The banks on either side of the river were broad. The view was unimpeded. It brought refreshment to the heart. Kulli smiled on seeing me happy and seated himself by the stones leading up to the summerhouse. I was tired; I sat beside him.

'Friend,' he said, 'how fresh the air smells.'

I liked being called friend. I much prefer friendship to the relationship of guru and disciple.

I agreed the air was fine. Kulli liked my agreeable response. He sounded yet more agreeable as he said, 'I can tell you sing. Sing something that suits the time and place.'

Only a connoisseur of music would ask for a song suiting time and place. I was flattered. Praise is always pleasing. What I didn't know before was that it makes you reckless. I began to sing. Kulli swayed from side to side. But I noticed with distress that Kulli wasn't keeping time to the music. 'Wah!' he said at a point that marked the pause. But it wasn't a true pause. What could have happened? I stopped singing.

'You are a high class singer,' Kulli said. 'I never knew.'

I swelled with pride. I reeled off a long list of ustads from whom I had learned to sing, one or two real, the others names I had heard of.

Kulli was impressed. 'You have learned from musicians who come to perform for the prince. Even among such illustrious singers your voice is special. It is not melody that pours from your throat but magic.'

What Kulli said must be true. I suppressed my elation.

Afternoon turned to evening. I should be getting home. 'Time to go,' I said.

Kulli sighed deeply. 'All right then, let's go.'

I was not familiar with the route Kulli took. I asked him about it and he said his house was not far off—that his house deserved to be purified by the dust on my feet.

I still considered myself a Brahmin in those days. It did not seem unnatural that the dust on my Brahmin feet should confer purification. I also thought about Kulli's body which was of course associated with the house Kulli wanted me to purify. I realized that people read vile motives into the kind-hearted statements Kulli made and that purifying Kulli's house and body would restore Kulli's reputation. I had seen nothing in his conduct which was untoward. Announcing Kulli's worthiness by visiting his house seemed an excellent idea. I walked quietly by Kulli's side. His house lay near the crossroads past the shops. Kulli unlocked the door and led me in. I was struck by the simplicity of the furnishings. Clearly this was a scholar yogi who lived in a modest hut among yapping hyenas. 'I live alone in this house,' Kulli said. 'I have no wife and no children. I own a little land and two traps. I live to please myself, but this does not please my neighbours. If I have a weakness or two what is that to others? It's my money that I spend.'

What he said made perfect sense.

'Fortunately there are people like you and me who aren't intimidated by gossip-mongers,' Kulli said. He offered me a paan tenderly, adding a little squeeze as our fingers brushed. 'Just like a brother-in-law,' I thought. Since Kulli belonged to my wife's town, he was entitled to tease me as a brother-in-law would. A strange kind of happiness came over Kulli when he saw I was not displeased. 'Come and have sweets with me tomorrow. You don't have to tell others about the invitation; people are only too ready to misunderstand. Come by nine.' He added meekly, 'Grace should be bestowed on the needy too.'

I couldn't understand the irony in his words just as people today don't understand the irony in mine. I accepted the invitation and got up to leave.

'How wonderfully the paan juice traces your lips,' he said, 'turning them into daggers.'

Kulli spoke with feeling, but I understood his words as the brother-in-law's teasing of the bridegroom. I smiled happily. Kulli accompanied me to the main road before taking his leave. He reminded me that we were to meet at nine the next day.

I joined my palms in acknowledgement.

Chandrika had been waiting by a roadside mound all this while. 'You took your own sweet time, Babu,' Chandrika said. 'I was hoping somebody hadn't played a trick on you.'

'No trick has been played on me, Chandrika, but we have a little deceiving of our own to do. When Mother-in-law asks, say we were together all the time.'

Chandrika agreed. I was still thinking about Kulli; I neglected to put things to Chandrika in a way he could grasp.

Mother-in-law was waiting for our return. When I went in to change clothes, she asked Chandrika to describe the places we had visited.

'I went nowhere, only to the perfume seller's for perfumed massage oil,' Chandrika said, too late to catch himself.

That was the clue Mother-in-law required. 'Did your Babu send you for the perfumed oil?'

'Yes,' Chadrika answered, feeling remorse at having said more than he should have.

'And afterwards?' she asked.

Chandrika was alert now. 'We went to the fort.'

'Did you see the seven-storey house there?'

'Yes.'

'Did you go to the big pond?'

'Yes.'

'Did you visit the Thousand-Treed garden?'

'Yes, everyone stood gazing at the trees a long time.'

Mother-in-law seized a solid walking stick and waved it at him. 'You crazy Afghan! Give me the full account or this stick will leave your face disfigured. Tell me where you went.'

'I am just a servant, Mother. Don't beat me. Ask my master.'

She had no need to ask. All became clear to her. When I emerged from my room, I saw Chandrika standing by Mother-in-law's side. She flashed a glance at me as if I was a pariah.

Then she went inside. I came out onto the road determined to sort things out. Chandrika followed me in tears. 'I won't stay here any longer,' he said.

'Will you admit defeat so easily? At least treat me to a few days of perfumed oil massage.'

Sobbing and whimpering, Chandrika described how the conversation with Mother-in-law had gone. I felt disgraced.

'They will stoop to anything. They are low enough to pry information out of a servant. Go ahead, use a full bottle of perfumed oil for your massage. Let them find out what class you are even though you hail from a village.'

I came to the inner courtyard and asked Chandrika to spread a mat for me. Mother-in-law watched my agitated countenance for a while before returning to her room. Chandrika laid the mat out and brought the bottle of perfumed oil. I pointed to my chest. That's where the massage was to begin. Chandrika shook the perfumed oil out as if it were water. He used up twenty rupees worth in no time, patting it liberally over my chest. 'That's all there is, Babu,' he said. For a moment, I felt the shock of such waste. Then I mastered myself. The smell of the perfume spread all around. Father-in-law came out of his room sniffing the fragrance. I greeted him boisterously. 'Be careful,' he said smiling. 'Such smells draw them down. The houris will be after you.'

Waves of perfume lappled against the walls of the inner rooms. Mother-in-law came out again.

Chandrika was absorbed in massaging me.

'Is that cologne you are using?'

'Perfumed oil,' I replied.

'How much did it cost?'

I answered calmly, 'Twenty rupees.'

'How often do you get massaged like this?'

'On alternate days,' I replied in the same calm tone.

'What benefit does such a massage confer?'

'It makes one broad-chested.'

My physique was broad since childhood, but Mother-in-law believed me that the cause lay in perfumed oil massages.

'What kind of monthly salary does your father get?' she asked.

It would have been embarrassing to tell her; my father's salary was pitifully small. But the world shines with false glory. I said in a robust voice, 'My father's income flows from many sources. We never know what flow will swell it at what time.'

On hearing this, Mother-in-law began to sob. 'Couldn't the father, who spends twenty rupees a day on perfumed oil for his son's massage, bring jewellery for his daughter-in-law worth two thousand rupees? I was a fool to have agreed to the marriage.'

I found it reassuring that we were on to a new subject. In any case, the perfumed oil had all been rubbed in. Continuing the massage would have made sparks fly from dry skin. I told Chandrika to stop.

Silence fell over the house in which, as the poet says, not a bee buzzed. It grew to be dinnertime, but I was not called in to eat. I tried to fix my mind on the ascetic verses of the *Charpat Panjrika*. To no avail. If the wind had turned against me so soon how would the rest of the visit pass? My wife's younger bother (now himself a father of several children) was four years old at that time. He started to cry for some reason and Chandrika sprang to his feet thinking it was the call to dinner. All grew quiet again.

'How do you feel?' I asked him.

'Babu, back home I would have been done with my dinner and the first round of sleep.'

'There's more variety to the food here,' I countered.

'But no millet and garbanzo cooked in oil.'

Just then Mother-in-law's servant came out to announce that food was ready.

Not a word was spoken during dinner. We could count each other's breaths. I ate mechanically and retired to my room.

When everyone had finished eating, my wife came into my room as on the previous night. What was missing tonight was the poetry in her gait. She offered me paan indifferently. I moved over to make room for her. She sat at the end of the bed and massaged my feet. Then she lay down on her half of the bed. I could guess why she felt distant, but I kept quiet. I knew her soft heart would prompt her to speak. After some moments of silence, she said the perfume was so strong she couldn't sleep.

'It's because you have no experience of such things. Do you remember the story of the fishwife? She was late returning from the river. She saw a gardener's hut in the king's garden and decided to spend the night in the hut. The garden was fragrant with flowers. The fishwife tossed and turned. She couldn't bear their fragrance. Then she remembered her fish basket. She drew the basket close, leaned her head against it and fell asleep immediately.'

My wife didn't like that. 'So I am a fishwife, am I?'

'When did I deny you were a Brahmin scholar? I just narrated a story people tell.'

'Do you think I eat fish?' she asked.

'It's not a matter of what you eat but of how things smell. Consider your greasy hair, for example. It smells so bad it makes me nauseous.'

'Do you take me for a whore? Must I be powdering and perfuming myself all the time?'

'You are not a she-goat either to be smelly all the time.'

My wife bounded from the bed. 'I am happy to go if that's what you wish.'

She paused waiting for my response.

'It's not by my wish alone,' I said laying the tenderness on, 'it's by your wish too that you share a bed with me. Decide for yourself what it is you want.'

My wife said nothing. Her face flushed from the insult. She left the bedroom door open as she walked out.

I said to myself, 'New day!'

Seven

There was a lot going on when I woke up the next morning. My four-year-old brother-in-law was screaming from the beating Mother-in-law gave him. Father-in-law had slipped in the latrine; the servant was engaged in washing the muck off him. Three bullocks had strayed into the courtyard. My wife went to drive them out. She struck one of them so hard that a horn broke. Someone ran to the astrologer to find out what the penance for the sacrilege would be. The maidservant's rope snapped and the brass bucket dropped into the well. The supply for the household was almost finished; there was no fresh rope to draw out more water. The neighbours promised to help but only after they had replenished their own supplies. Meanwhile Chandrika was nowhere to be seen.

As I opened my eyes, I heard Mother-in-law saying, 'Misfortunes never come singly.' The proverb was familiar to me. I imagined Mother-in-law had been told about my conduct the previous night and quoted the proverb so I would overhear. I took my time getting up. Everyone was still running about. One by one I learned about all the disasters that had befallen the family. Chandrika had still not appeared. The servant who had finished helping Father-in-law clean up came up to inform me that Chandrika had left. He had no money, but he was going to walk along the railway track till it reached our village. 'Tell the Babu not to worry,' he had said. 'If I had spoken to him first he would not have let me go.' The servant added that Chandrika expected to lose his job but was counting on his skills as a farmhand to find work again.

The aftershocks of the previous night must have affected Chandrika too. Was it my wife who spoke to him? 'Was Chandrika around,' I asked the servant, 'when the bullock's horn was broken?' The servant nodded yes.

We were still talking about the commotion when I saw it was eight o'clock. Time to set out for Kulli's. I dressed and went out. I saw a young woman near the well with a pot full of water, an auspicious sign. Further up the road, I saw a calf feeding from its mother, another auspicious sign. Some people greeted me as I walked, complimenting me on my health and good looks. I toned down my expression to one of modesty and continued on my way to Kulli's house. I found that he was already out on the road. On seeing me, he advanced towards me the way Nadir Shah's army advanced towards Mathura certain of victory. After all the auspicious signs I had received, it was easy for me to radiate gladness in response. This warmed Kulli's heart. 'Come,' he said and led me inside.

There was a large mirror on the wall hung with small garlands at each corner. He put his arm around my waist, and when we looked in the mirror we seemed to be garlanded even though we wore no flowers. I was pleased with the effect. Kulli looked at my reflection in the mirror and smiled. I smiled back. 'This is good,' Kulli said.

He hurried into an inner room and came back with a tray of sweets. He set the tray on a high wooden platform, brought a jug of water and poured some in a glass. He stood watching me eat. When I finished eating, he poured me some more water to wash my hands with and a hand towel. He also offered me paan.

I sat down on his well-made bed covered with a small galeecha. Kulli took out a bottle of cologne. 'I had this sent to me; it isn't perfumed oil because we aren't masseurs.' I looked at him in innocent bewilderment. Whatever could he mean? Kulli for his part went pale. His features lost their composure. He wiggled towards me on the bed, then wiggled back. I wondered if he had taken ill. He cast a look of longing perhaps in my direction. 'I had better lock the door.'

But his voice died even as he uttered these words. I grew afraid, not of him but for him. I didn't think that Kulli could injure me in any way, but I feared that his illness—for that is what it must be—would bring him harm.

'Shouldn't we call a doctor?'

'You are cruel,' he said.

I tried to understand the connection between his wiggling and my cruelty. It made no sense.

'I can use force if...' and he wiggled towards me again.

I burst out laughing. Kulli remained where he was, but he said indistinctly, like a person drowning in a well, 'I love you.'

'I love you, too,' I replied.

'Come. Let's go then,' he said and drew himself to his full height.

I didn't know where I was to go.

'Have you never ever...?'

The less I understood the angrier I got. 'Tell me in plain words where you want me to go.'

Kulli had nothing more to say. He suddenly became spineless, like a limp rag.

'Goodbye,' I said as I left.

Thus ended my first encounter with Kulli. I came home. I was greeted with utter silence. I might as well not have been present. The civil disobedience directed towards me made me think of Father. One small move of his had turned this entire household upside down. But I had neither wit nor wisdom to make any move in response to the turn the situation was taking.

'Where did you go?' Mother-in-law asked as if it were a simple, casual question.

It would be wrong to tell a lie. 'I was at Kulli's.' I didn't think it appropriate to volunteer any more information.

Mother-in-law stared at me. Her doubts about me had all been confirmed the previous evening. No additional supporting evidence was necessary.

I decided to seize the initiative. 'It wasn't just the bullock's horn which was broken, I too suffered an injury. I have been crippled. (I was thinking of how I had been crippled by Chandrika's departure.) You have found out about a remedy for injury to the bullock. What about a remedy for injury to my foot?'

'Where? Let me see.' Mother-in-law bent down and felt along my foot.

'Ask your daughter to help you.'

'Beti,' Mother-in-law said to her softly, 'You seem to have sprained his foot while you were trying to massage it last night. Take a look. Why didn't you tell me about it earlier?'

'Where does it hurt?' My wife seemed perplexed.

I had a permanent swelling on the big toe of my right foot from playing football. Mother-in-law saw that this big toe was fatter and reached down to feel it. 'This must be where,' she said to my wife. 'Doesn't this look swollen, Beti?'

Her daughter said with worry in her voice, 'Yes, that's where,' and she followed her mother in taking hold of this toe.

'Son, don't you think we should make lime and turmeric paste for the swelling?'

'They have bowed at my feet,' I reflected. 'They want forgiveness. I will let the Chandrika matter go.' To them I said with a yogi's equanimity. 'Don't bother.'

'Sweet is peace after conflict,' I thought to myself. 'The other matter can wait.' My wife began preparing a poultice of lime and turmeric.

Eight

Father-in-law objected when I asked for perfumed oil the following day. 'Perfumed oil can't be used daily. We are ordinary people. We barely manage ghee for food at a rupee a pound; perfumed oil runs at eighty rupees. Mustard oil will have to do.'

'There goes the plan to take my wife home,' I thought. The pull towards her was strong. I may have mumbled verses about the ephemerality of pleasures in her hearing, but she never found me holding back as far as she was concerned. Nor was I accomplished in arts and letters as she had imagined. She felt deceived.

My money was gone. Father-in-law guessed rightly that I had no more than travel expenses left and that I couldn't send for perfumed oil on my own. He knew that even the children of the rich don't receive daily massages of perfumed oil.

I was trapped. I wanted to be like Father and say I was ready to remarry. But like Kulli, I would lose heart. I might recite 'Who is wife to you? Who son?' by day, but the truth was I couldn't bear to be away from my wife a single night. I was a modern lover. I had declared my love to her in countless words. She knew my remarrying was out of the question.

During the day I pretended to be coolly indifferent; at night I turned into an ardent spouse. My wife endured the tumult of her own feelings in silence.

I decided to bring matters to a head. For her own reasons, or so it seemed to me, my wife refused to act as an inferior. In particular, she was proud of her knowledge of Hindi. She conceded the possibility that I might be well informed on other subjects, but as far as Hindi literature was concerned, she counted me an idiot. I, having no clue to the range of her understanding, found her superior attitude annoying. 'You keep talking up Hindi,' I said, 'but what's there of any worth in Hindi letters?'

'You barely speak the language. What would you know of letters?'

'Are you saying I don't know Hindi?'

'Your Baisvari dialect reveals how provincial you are. Do you know the Khari Boli speech of Delhi?'

I had never heard of Khari Boli. Nor did the names of supreme writers such as Pandit Mahavir Prasad Dwivedi, Pandit Ayodhya Singh Upadhyay and Babu Maithili Sharan Gupta mean anything to me at that time. In a single breath, my wife reeled off the names of twenty Khari Boli poets and scholars. I was awed the way a reader is awed by an essay filled with quotations. I could not doubt the scope of her learning or the loftiness of thought to which she had access. I began to understand why merely addressing the deity with a thousand names exerts a powerful effect.

Things were quiet for a while. Obviously there were no more massages with perfumed oil. Mother-in-law was keeping count of the days to my departure. My wife, meanwhile, continued to dazzle me with her wide knowledge of literature. I needed to leave but could not bear to think of heading off to the railway station away from her.

A musical evening was organized about this time. On an earlier occasion, Mother-in-law had praised her daughter's voice. No woman, young or old, Mother-in-law had said, could match the quality of her daughter's singing. I was happy to be able to take in her performance before returning home.

People began to gather. The sounds of drumming could be heard—deep sounds, not shrill beats such as women often like. Some of the men who arrived seemed less interested in the music than in the beautiful women to be admired. Trays of paan were passed around. The men ate paan and began to compare the qualities of the available and unavailable women.

The singing began with ghazals. The audience was hard on singers who did not know courtly ghazals but sang devotional songs instead. The singers of devotional songs were mostly older women. They were drawn to what the fashionable younger women sang, but did not know the new style. It is no different today in the field of literature.

I wonder why we have been quick to accept English ways, but are far slower with the ghazal. Why is it that English food and clothing and sitting arrangements have became our own, but the Persian language and the poetry of Hafiz remain unfamiliar? Why didn't these older women adopt Urdu ghazals the way the younger women fresh from college have adopted European ways of courting, of playing the piano and of working for the uplift of 'backward' women?

What we should have passed on to our daughters was the splendour of our own culture. What had been passed on instead led to stifled thought and cultural indigestion. Raja Rammohan Roy was the first to discover this. Well, let the English look after the half-educated among us. I turned my mind to the ghazal singing.

There was a steady stream of commentary from the audience. Who was the lead singer? Who were the accompanists? Whose were the well-trained voices? The men in the audience were stirred by the beauty of the ghazals and the charm of the professional singers. Some of the singers may have been ladies of easy virtue, but their allure was irresistible.

My wife sat quietly to one side, the way major poets sit at literary gatherings. I wasn't aware that it was her the crowd was waiting to hear.

When she began to sing, she chose the crown jewel of devotional songs, the adoration of Lord Ram which begins: '*Shri Ram Chandra Kripalu bhaju man haran bhavbhay darunam*' ('Sing praise of Ram, who banishes terror of being'). The listeners held their breath. She sang the line about Lord Ram's incomparable beauty, his body a denser blue than the azure sky. My jaw dropped. Could my Bengali condescension have kept me from noticing the depth of her accomplishment?

She followed with the ghazal: '*Agar hai chaah milne ki to hardam lau lagaataa jaa*' ('If you desire to meet let your mind dwell on me'). The audience was ready to renounce the world for the love this stirred in them. People cast questioning glances at one another. Whom was this song dedicated to? Didn't they know? Obviously, it was dedicated to me, but many in the audience seemed secretly pleased for reasons I did not understand.

The next song was a fast-paced dadra:

Sasuji ka chhokda, meri thadi pe rakh diya haath

('My mother-in-law's son laid his hand on my chin

I could have slapped him straight, but I held my pain in').

One of the listeners didn't like the lyrics. 'Why should she object to her own husband? He must be that sort,' the fellow said aloud. Little did the listener know that the husband sat next to him. Another member of the audience turned to me and said the lyrics didn't have to be about the husband. They could be about the brother-in-law. A third listener confirmed that the lyrics were indeed about a naughty brother-in-law. I breathed a sigh of relief.

The singing ended in a little while. The men stretched themselves and got ready to depart. The women, too, left one by one. Only members of our household were left. My wife sang beautifully; her knowledge of Hindi was profound. My talents in these fields were undeveloped. There was no shame in acknowledging my shortcomings. I penned a note to my father. 'I am going on to Calcutta to catch up with my studies. Please visit here whenever you wish. I am well.' I dropped the letter off at the post office and began to pack my things.

'Why are you packing all of a sudden?'

'I am going to Calcutta.'

Mother-in-law's face went pale. She had intended to talk to me about her daughter's skills as a singer, but she grew confused. 'Packing is work for the servants to do and it's too soon for you to leave. What will your father think? What will the neighbours think? We will be disgraced because we couldn't offer hospitality to our son-in-law for longer than a week.'

'Let the disgrace be my lot then.'

'How? How would you be disgraced?'

'That's for you to understand.'

Mother-in-law paused. A look of comprehension dawned on her face. She realized I was aware that news of my time with Kulli had reached her. 'I had warned you,' she said, 'that Kulli was not the right sort of person for you.'

'Let's drop this topic of whether it is Kulli who is not the right person for me or whether it is your daughter.'

I spoke in a measured tone, but Mother-in-law began to sob. Her daughter joined in, sobbing along more softly. 'You are God to her. I wouldn't lie,' Mother-in-law said. 'See the fire burning under the stove? Let me burn, too, if I speak untruth. If you told my daughter to swallow live coals, she would. You can think of her as you wish, but the women who just left were full of praise for her.'

'That is why I am setting out.'

Packing one's own bags at the in-laws is a sign of displeasure. Mother-in-law thought I was sore over perfumed oil for massages. 'We had no cash to pay with, but we can arrange to get the perfumed oil for you tomorrow.'

'It isn't essence of perfume I seek but essence of being,' I answered.

Mother-in-law looked puzzled.

'I have my studies to finish,' I said. 'I need time to prepare.'

She said with relief, 'So you really are going to Calcutta.

I thought it was a ruse to get back to your village. I was worried about the plague, too. Finishing your studies is a good thing. One does have to think of the future.' She asked the servant to finish my packing.

My bags were ready. The horse cart arrived. I took leave of my in-laws in time to make the Rae Bareli train.

Nine

Five years passed. I made frequent trips to the town of my in-laws, but never came across Kulli. Meanwhile I was burning to master Hindi. Nobody knew Hindi in the Bengal countryside in which I lived. The soldiers in the Raja's army spoke the Western Braj[3] which I knew already, but there were no users of the Hindi of Delhi. I entered subscriptions for the two Hindi monthlies published at the time, *Saraswati* and *Maryada*. The very look of *Saraswati* communicated dignity, of *Maryada* it was the opposite.[4] I would read the magazines and could catch the feeling behind a piece of writing, but I couldn't write anything of my own. The grammar of Hindi was quite different from the grammar of Braj or Avadhi. I discovered that there is nothing diligence cannot accomplish. I would stay up till two or three in the morning construing sentences of Delhi Hindi on the basis of what I knew of Sanskrit, English and Bengali. I was especially happy when I could figure out a rule of Hindi grammar that

[3] Braj is the language spoken in the region around Mathura. It was the dominant literary language before the rise of Khari Boli.

[4] Saraswati is the goddess of learning; 'maryada' in Hindi means dignity.

did not derive from any of the languages I knew. It was akin to the joy of knowing God.

I overcame many hurdles in this way. I took Mahavir Prasad Dwivedi to be my guru and received instruction as Eklavya did rather than as Arjun did.[5] I wrote 'A Bud of Jasmine'[6] before I had completed my education in Hindi grammar, but I found out afterwards that I had divined the rules correctly. It is said about world-famous poets that they began to write poetry from the age of seven or eight. This was true of me, too, except that in my case I was writing poetry in Bengali. The words I penned then have entered the Great Unknown; no trace of the juvenile compositions remains. When I was sixteen or seventeen I began to feel that Fortune was ranged against me. My response was not to seek safety in money or big houses or the patronage of politicians, in superstition or in magic. Those who run after such things lose their life, those who pursue livingness itself are not denied acquaintance with life's mystery. Enough said.

I dropped out of school once I realized that the goal of schooling was gainful employment. I had no clear sense of a grander purpose, but utilitarian ends did not seem sufficient. Later my large-hearted friends provided me hints of the vastness for which I had sacrificed petty employment. But at the time I speak of, I was a low-level member of the Raja's administration. I was fed up dealing with correspondence

---

[5] By inwardly accepting Dwivedi as his model as the outcaste Eklavya had accepted Dronacharya. Arjuna, by contrast, was an acknowledged pupil of Dronacharya and received direct instruction.

[6] 'Juhi ki kali'.

and accounts when the Raja took it into his head to start a theatre group.

The ideas of great ones don't take long to be executed. The head clerk of the law court was selected as the lead. I auditioned along with the other employees. I was given a simple Sanskrit song to prepare, simple because Bengalis are thought to have atrocious pronunciation in Sanskrit.

I memorized the song carefully. The Raja was present at the audition. He liked my singing and arranged for me to start receiving voice lessons. As my musical skills improved, I became an increasingly popular performer. Unfortunately, my popularity also made me the object of envy.

There was a violent outbreak of influenza about this time. My father had passed away a year earlier; I was compelled to look for work to support the family. Otherwise, I too would have lived dreamily like other young people, wishing happiness to myself and to all other living beings.

I received a telegram: 'Your wife is gravely ill. Come immediately.' I was twenty-two. I became aware of the intensity of her love just as she was ready to take leave of life. The newspapers had informed us about the ravages of the epidemic. I travelled to the riverbank in Dalmau and waited. The Ganga was swollen with dead bodies. At my in-laws' house, I learned that my wife had passed away. My cousin had come over from my ancestral village to help with my wife's illness, but he had taken ill himself and returned home. I left for our ancestral village the very next day. As I was walking towards my house, I saw my cousin's corpse being carried to the cremation site. My head grew dizzy; I sat down on the ground to take a hold of myself.

At home I found my cousin's wife lying ill on a pallet. 'How far has the funeral procession travelled?' she asked. I had nothing to say. They had four sons and a baby girl who was still nursing. The oldest child lived with me in Bengal and went to school there. My uncle was the head of the family. He, too, contracted influenza. 'What madness brought you here?' he said to me.

Words cannot describe how pitiful the scene was, how helpless, how tender. But I had no tenderness left after the death of my wife and my cousin. I said in a dry voice, 'Get well and I will take the whole family to Bengal.'

This was my first opportunity to serve those who were ill. Since then there has been no dearth in my life of calls for such service. Sister-in-law passed away on the third day after my cousin's death. The nursing child was also sick. I slept that night holding her. She, too, passed away in the morning. I buried her in the riverbank. Then Uncle died. One more corpse to cart to the Ganga. Sister-in-law's three sons contracted fever. Somehow I was able to nurse them back to health. This was the strangest time in my life. My family disappeared in the blink of an eye. All our sharecroppers and labourers died, the four who worked for my cousin as well as the two who worked for me. My cousin's eldest son was fifteen years old, my young daughter a year old. In whichever direction I turned, I saw darkness.

After I had attended to the affairs of my household, I went to my in-laws'. In spite of the suffering, I was able to keep my mind steady. I would go sit on a mound by the Ganga and watch the file of corpses brought to the river. It is impossible to describe my feelings. The mound of sadhus in Dalmau is famous for its height. The Ganga made a sharp turn below it. The corpses were laid together. Sometimes I would think of the ascetic sadhus, sometimes of the ephemerality of the world.

One day Kulli appeared at the mound; he had asked people where he might find me. He looked sad at first, sensing my grief and bearing condolences, then his face broke into a smile. I saw that pure smile and realized he was a true friend. 'I am aware that you loved Manohara[7] deeply,' he said. 'God brings us to our senses by depriving us of what we desire. You are wiser than me. You know such things already. Enjoyment is fine in itself, but the main thing is to come to a good end.'

I was staring at the brick floor of the sadhu's hut. 'Those who are dead have found peace already,' he said. 'Those who have beheld death seek peace as you do. This mound of sadhus is far from the town and, in feeling, far from the cremation grounds. It is as if an ascetic sadhu settled here after he died. His immortal presence makes it an abode of peace.'

Kulli's words had a soothing effect. 'Would you like to come to Ramgiri Maharaj's ashram? You have probably visited there already.' 'No,' I said, 'I have never been there.'

We set out for the ashram.

[7] Nirala's wife, Manohara Devi.

Ten

I returned to my job shortly thereafter. One day a sadhu turned up. He would sit under a tree with a smoky fire going and his fire tongs[8] stuck into the ground. In general, I had an independent way of looking at things, but I had become even more sceptical reading books on my own and listening to reformers such as Swami Vivekananda and Swami Ramtirth. The aim of a sadhu's meditation is transcendental. There are many ancient ways of approaching the transcendental. When a person apprehends truth his understanding becomes true. What is affected is not one proposition or another, but the process of understanding itself. At this stage, the difference between ancient and modern methods holds little significance for him. I was a modern. I had read books by sadhus who objected to the use of intoxicants. But the sadhus I came across smoked ganja and stumbled about on our roads. They were not learned in English like Swami Vivekananda or Swami Ramtirth. Nor were their students learned enough in English to object to ganja. Lofty understanding has no further need of words. The stumbling

[8] The tongs itinerant sadhus carry with them to help in arranging coals and building a fire.

sadhus smoked to overcome fatigue. As poison can be an antidote to disease, ganja can be an antidote to mere living. The sadhus valued character but not pointless asceticism; not urinating or defecating for a week could never be signs of spiritual accomplishment.

The family man fluent in English seeks a sadhu who knows English. The family man is eager to learn the sadhu's views on things from Europe and America. The truth, on the other hand, has no particular interest in Europe or America. The street sadhus think the English-speaking sadhus are frauds, each sadhu lording it over his coterie of disciples. So here was this non-English speaking sadhu sitting under the tree looking to collect the train fare to the Jagannath temple in Puri. The Raja's household superintendent was favourably disposed towards the sadhu. He advised the Raja to help him out.

After the court offices closed, I would spend my evenings with the Raja. He was fond of music; he played the mridanga rather well. 'There is a sadhu visiting here,' the Raja said when I arrived at the royal mansion. 'Go take a look and tell me what you think.'

Rajas ask many people for their advice. Their eyes can't be everywhere, but they are all ears. They listen to various advisers and only then form their own opinion. I made an immediate declaration of my loyalty. 'Raja,' I said, 'there is no need to squander money from the treasury.'

My brain was full of unassimilated ideas readily found in utilitarian philosophies. The Raja smiled. I couldn't interpret the smile, but I did know I was his employee. I had been given an assignment. With the thought in my heart that not a rupee from the treasury should be wasted, I made my way to the sadhu.

He greeted me graciously upon my arrival. 'Please come sit.'

'These deceivers!' I thought to myself. 'Hey you! Why don't you find some work for yourself?' I said out loud.

I didn't know at the time that those who set out to seek God and realize him burn off their karmas. There's only God left in their thoughts.

'I address you politely,' the sadhu said, 'but you respond with rudeness. What kind of work would you like me to do?'

'Hey, that's none of my concern. Is there nothing useful you can do in this wide world?'

'And who do you think keeps the wide world going?' the sadhu asked.

I had read about these imposters who talk big and perform magic tricks.

'Hey, you are not going to receive any rupees.'

'Come to your senses,' the sadhu said and pushed his fire tongs into the ground.

I felt the tongs press into my scalp. My head dropped. I was singed with fire. I realized my intention had been impure. But I still could not summon up respect for the sadhu.

He towered over me. 'Hey, are you the Raja or something?' The sadhu made the same mistake I had made. He, too, addressed me rudely. I tried to stay in the fight, like a wrestler not giving up under the weight of his opponent. 'No, I am not the Raja,' I answered.

The sadhu was having his fun with me. By 'Raja' he

meant Lord Ram who sustains the universe. I, of course, understood the Raja of whom I had just taken leave.

'If you are his servant,' the sadhu asked, 'why don't you speak as a servant should speak?'

Here the sadhu erred. A servant is Lord Ram as much as the master. There was the further complication that my chosen deity was Lord Shiva, not Lord Ram.

The sadhu wanted me to disengage before he would restore me to my senses. But it was not I who was fighting him, it was Lord Shiva. 'I will have you dismissed from service,' the sadhu threatened.

If I had wavered under the threat the sadhu would have prevailed. 'That will make me free,' I countered. It was not me but Lord Shiva who spoke, although I did not know this at the time.

The sadhu was astonished. How could a man with numerous children to support be so unconcerned? He began to weep. 'For you, Lord,' he said, 'I have been wandering through village and town. Is this how you mock me?'

I saw a light; I began to understand. I had seen this light while composing 'A Bud of Jasmine' and hadn't known what the light was.

When I was about to leave, the sadhu asked if we could travel the road together. But my pull was towards the world. I did not want knowledge alone. I also wanted to live out the karmas I must perform in the world. The sadhu felt the pain of our parting. He made a hollow moaning sound as if I had broken his body.

By the time I reached the Raja's mansion, I had forgotten

these things. I was thinking only of pleasing the Raja. 'What kind of man is he?' the Raja asked. 'You shouldn't be wasting money on such people,' I said. The Raja heard me and kept silent.

The superintendent came to the Raja in the morning and received permission to grant twenty rupees to the sadhu. The superintendent proffered the money to the sadhu as if he was doing the sadhu a favour. The sadhu refused the gift, 'The Raja himself visited me yesterday. I have made him angry.' He flung his fire tongs before the superintendent and started to walk away.

'The man who came to visit you is an ordinary employee. He is not the Raja.'

'You don't understand,' the sadhu said. 'He is the Raja all right.'

The superintendent did not know what to say. The sadhu left.

I crossed that way shortly afterwards. 'Did you tell the sadhu,' the superintendent asked me, 'that you were the true king?'

'I said no such thing,' I replied.

The superintendent was no less loyal to the Raja than I. 'You said something to the sadhu which made him refuse the Raja's money and fling his tongs away. I will make a report to the Raja immediately.'

Who will understand the difference between the person who bows before the universe and the person who bows before worldly authority?

The superintendent made a dramatic report to the Raja such as people make when they hear something second-hand.

'Did you tell the sadhu you were the Raja?' the Raja asked softly when I arrived.

I couldn't bring myself to answer in words appropriate to the occasion. The Raja, too, seemed to me a mere mortal. 'I said that a Raja's employee was no less than the Raja.' The Raja understood this sort of monism well. The great bureaucrats of India have disseminated such understanding successfully.

I was let off on that occasion, but the dilemmas in my life persisted. One night around eleven, I was walking from the Raja's mansion to my own rooms. I saw the superintendent walking in my direction near the elephant house, about a mile from where he lived. It was well known that the superintendent drank and those who drink get into other mischief as well. But the world is concerned with image. Anything which disturbs that image is a threat. I was surprised to see the superintendent. He was surprised to see me, perhaps also because he had complained about me to the Raja. I was baffled that he should be out this late in an unfamiliar part of town. I could smell the alcohol on his breath.

The next day I mentioned this meeting to the Raja. I was making light conversation. Everybody knew the superintendent liked his drink. They laughed.

But the great ones have diverse ways of relating to their inferiors. Some time later, I was commanded to go the Krishna temple and swear before the deity that I had seen the superintendent drunk.

The superintendent sent me a directive: 'Say I was not drunk.' He was a practical man. He also arranged for the elephant keeper to be his witness. The elephant keeper was to say that an evil spirit had entered into the superintendent's son and that the superintendent needed the elephant keeper's help in driving out the spirit. The elephant keeper was to swear to this on the Koran.

The elephant keeper was not asked to be present on the appointed day. Only the superintendent and I went to the temple. I swore to what I had smelled on the superintendent's breath. The superintendent swore he had not been drinking.

When the swearing and counter-swearing were over, I tendered my resignation. I wrote the Raja a personal note saying he had no right to make me swear before the god I worshipped. I added that I had never asked for the superintendent's dismissal.

The superintendent told the Raja that I had made up the story about his drinking. I wanted, he said, to get back at him for favouring a sadhu I did not like. The superintendent reminded the Raja that he too had left off drinking when the Raja gave up alcohol. The Raja had taken note of the superintendent's pursuit of virtue and declared him worthy of mystical initiation from the royal guru.

My resignation was rejected. The Raja penned a note to me: 'It is folly to abandon a definite position for uncertain prospects.'

'Let me serve the uncertain,' I said in reply. 'I will instruct my successor in the work I do.' I also requested the remainder of my salary.

Many people came to say goodbye. The assistant manager who had frequently been accused of taking bribes claimed I had been the one honest man in the Raja's administration.

The others, he said, looked to their advantage and nodded their heads in assent to the Raja's wishes.

I sold my belongings and returned to my village with my nephew.

The Non-Cooperation movement was at its height. The labourers winnowing the landlord's grain would break into cries of 'Long live Mahatma Gandhi!' in the hope that their bonded labour would end. The more modern government employees, policemen and landlords mocked the peasants, calling them swine. Some inert wealthy citizens read through half a dozen newspapers daily and offered their wise counsel to anyone who would hear. 'This Mahatma,' one of them said to me, 'has proved that if you turn a spinning wheel at one end, chapatis will come out the other end.'

I was idle. The editors of *Saraswati* rejected the poems and essays I submitted. The journal *Prabha* dealt exclusively with well-known poets and litterateurs. I went into their office to inquire. I was told they only published poets of the calibre of Maithili Sharan Gupt, leader of the vanguard of India's destiny. They named a few other writers worthy of publication. I returned home disappointed. There was no way of earning money. I had four young nephews to feed. I asked the gentleman who had joked about Gandhiji's magic to buy me a takua on his next visit to Kanpur.

A caste of weavers lived adjacent to my house. I began to sit by their looms to learn the art of weaving. 'Why would you, a Brahmin,' they said, 'want to learn our labourer's craft? You should be reciting the story of Lord Krishna to worshippers.'

The gentleman who went to Kanpur returned without my takua. 'I forgot,' he said. 'I was in a hurry.'

I had no peace of mind. Fathers eager to marry off their daughters would descend upon me, each one describing his daughter as a goddess. I tried to escape by moving to my in-laws' in Dalmau, but the population of seekers for eligible grooms was even greater there. I was sitting alone on the riverbank one day when Kulli happened to walk by. The passage of time had made him thoughtful. He greeted me courteously as before. He was under the impression that I was now an important social worker. He himself had begun to read the newspapers. He had given up his job as salesman of revenue stamps in protest against British rule. He began speaking of Gandhiji. I responded to his questions about current politics with the little that I knew.

He grew impassioned. 'Tell me what to do with my life.'

'Throw yourself in the Ganga.'

'What are you saying?' he asked.

'Are you capable of drowning or not?' I said by way of reply.

'What difference would that make? Be sensible.'

'I have forgotten how.'

'What were you doing by the riverbank?'

'Sitting idly. I hadn't come here expecting you.'

Kulli had no idea of the volcano raging inside me. He stared at me a while, then left.

Eleven

After many turns of the wheel, I became a fully formed literary person. My fame spread in the field of poetry as rats fan out in a field of grain. I became known to peasants and landlords. Within a year, Kalidasa arrived from Calcutta[9] and Shri Harsha from Allahabad[10] to redeem Hindi poetry. Poets of the old school joined forces and mounted attacks against the new style, but they suffered defeat after defeat. The reason was they weren't using brain power. Their guns fired blanks. It has always been so: the old school loses out against the moderns.

I returned to my village a name in Hindi poetry, the object of wonderment among literary critics. From my village I went to Dalmau. Kulli met me there. He read the papers and knew of my reputation. He treated me with respect, feeling pride at his friend's making a name in the world. He did not speak of the poets of his region as before; they did not rate high in the newspapers he was now reading. Besides, they were court poets, not independents like me.

[9] Banarasi Das Chaturvedi, Hindi critic and writer (1892–1985).
[10] Mahavir Prasad Dwivedi, Hindi critic and writer (1864–1938). Editor of *Saraswati* (1903–1920).

'Haven't you married again?' he asked suddenly.

'I didn't feel the need for it,' I answered.

'How do you manage?'

'The way a widow manages.'

'Widows get into all kinds of immorality.'

'I must be doing the same,' I said.

My answer pleased Kulli. 'But you know it is a sin.'

'So long as there is virtue, too, the sins don't matter. A spark of fire can burn down a barn.'

'What is your view of society?' he asked.

'The traditions that come down to us are not of equal merit.'

'What is your view of Hindu-Muslim relations?'

'A Hindu can become a Muslim but not the other way around.'

Kulli seemed satisfied with my answers. I did not know it then, but he was comparing his own life experiences with my views and finding that they matched. 'There is a Muslim woman in my life,' he ventured. 'I love her, and for her part, she is willing to sacrifice her life for me. She wants to move in with me, but I am afraid of our guardians of morality.'

'All the guardians need is something to occupy themselves with.'

'So you think I should let her live with me?'

I had witnessed Hindu-Muslim riots in Calcutta. Newspapers devoted many columns to such questions. Over inflammatory articles, Munshi Navjadiklal[11] had Mahadev

---

[11] Navajadiklal Srivastava, manager of Balkrishna Press.

Babu[12] imprisoned for four months. I was one of those who garlanded Mahadev Babu when he came out of jail. The spirit of the times was in me. 'You must bring her home,' I said passionately.

Kulli was electrified by my response. 'These impotent guardians of Hinduism want to make the rest of us impotent too.'

'Present an example to them of how courageous people live.'

Kulli rushed away to his beloved's house to bring her home and set a suitable example.

---

[12] Mahadev Prasad Seth, owner of Balkrishna Press and publisher of Matwala.

Twelve

I moved to Lucknow soon afterwards. The Civil Disobedience movement was over; attention had shifted to the problem of the untouchables. I paid a visit to Dalmau and saw a new Kulli. He was a major figure in politics. Rae Bareli was the centre of political activity; Kulli had participated in various protests there. Dalmau was chosen as the site for manufacturing salt in defiance of British law. Kulli telephoned to say the police were going to fire on protesters using real bullets. The protest site was moved from the town of Dalmau to the city of Rae Bareli so the police action would draw notice.

Kulli had begun to hate lawyers, policemen, government employees, temple pandits, landlords. He felt outraged by many Brahmins, too.

He greeted me as a political leader greets a colleague.

'How is the work going in your district?' he asked.

'What work?'

'The work we are engaged in,' he said with perplexity.

'Political?'

'Yes, the revolution.'

'That's over,' I said.

'How can things go forward then?'

'I don't know which move leads to what outcome. I don't go along with everything. I mix in what I've read and heard with what I think on my own.'

Kulli was satisfied. When one becomes a lamb, the other becomes confident of being the wolf. That's the real reason meekness is praised in the world. I showed Kulli I was ordinary. He began to feel himself extraordinary in comparison.

'I brought her home,' he volunteered.

'Whom?'

'The Muslim woman.'

'You have followed my advice. Remember when I told you to jump in the Ganga and you stood undecided on the riverbank?'

'How have I jumped into the Ganga?'

'The ancient books speak of woman as a river. The Ganga is the most excellent among rivers. You have brought the most excellent woman into your house.'

'But people here don't acknowledge her properly.'

I gazed at Kulli's walking stick. 'They will acknowledge her when they see what kind of person she is. Nobody doubts that what you have in your hand is a walking stick.'

Kulli looked at his walking stick appreciatively. 'People make things difficult for her. I sent her for a darshan of Pathvari[13] Devi. She was not even permitted to reach the temple door.

'The goddess was instructing you. She is more the

[13] Goddess of the path.

goddess of those who wish to approach her than of those who think her power works only in the temple.'

'Ah, yes. She is goddess of the path, not of the temple. You are wise as Lord Ganesha,' Kulli said, and drew an elephant trunk in the air.

'Lord Ganesha...' I began with half a mind to confound Kulli, 'Lord Ganesha is as stupid as he is wise. In Bengali they call a person "foolish as an elephant". A friend of mine went on a tiger hunt. He shot a tiger and covered it over with leaves. Then he climbed back onto the bamboo platform from which he had been hunting. He wanted to shoot a deer for his supper before heading home. But instead of deer, a herd of wild elephants came his way. You know no animal is more dangerous than a wild elephant. The elephant can shake a man down from a tree as we shake down plums. It can also reach with its trunk and tear the branch on which the man stands. My friend was a seasoned hunter. Luckily the platform he was hunting from was high. As soon as he saw the lead elephant smelling him out on the platform, he dropped his gun over the pile of leaves covering the tiger. The elephant broke the gun into two. By then my friend had a found a high branch to climb onto. The elephant grew curious about the mound and brushed some leaves aside. As soon as it saw the tiger, it broke into a run and the other elephants followed. My friend was saved, though that may just be a matter of chance. There is a lesson to be learned nonetheless. Where elephants oppress you the skin of a tiger offers protection. Brains are superior to brawn.'

Kulli understood that the person who addressed him was not lacking in brains.

'I have started a school for untouchables. About forty students attend. They are children of tanners, street sweepers, washermen and toddy gatherers. I am the principal teacher. I get no help from the worthies of our town. I went to the chairman of the municipality. He said nothing to encourage me in my endeavours. The riverside colony of mixed-caste Brahmins is indifferent to my project. Government officials keep plotting against me. I may have to return to the donkey work I was doing before I joined the Non-Cooperation movement.'

Kulli will find a way to sustain his endeavour, I thought to myself, but I can be allowed some fun. I am descended from the Aryans who offered the soma elixir to the gods and whose progeny, as Kaka Kalelkar reminds us, are permitted the use of toddy.

I said excitedly, 'Write to Mahatma Gandhi.'

'At what address shall I write to him?' Kulli spoke with relief as if I had shown him the way. He took out his notebook and jotted down the address. 'Is there anyone else I should write to?'

'Yes,' I said. 'Write to Jawaharlal Nehru.'

'Is the address Anand Bhavan, Allahabad?'

'Or you could just write, Freedom House,[14] Allahabad,' I responded.

He noted this down too.

'Please come visit us,' he added. 'I can show you our work and you can meet my wife.'

---

[14] Nehru's residence was a centre of anti-colonial political activity, hence the speaker's suggestion of an alternate name for the residence.

'What colour is her skin? Light or dark?'

Kulli smiled. 'Judge for yourself.'

'Does she have any talents?' I asked like a fashionably modern person.

'She recites the Ramayana well,' Kulli answered gravely. 'She was just over at the Raja of Shivgarh's, who was pleased at her recitation.' I was tempted to ask whether the Raja had merely expressed pleasure or made a monetary gift as well, but I thought the question might seem rude.

'When will you visit the school?'

I wished to respond directly where untouchables were concerned. 'Tell me which day would be convenient for you. Shall we say the day after tomorrow? You could get word out and I could meet the full assembly of children.'

Kulli agreed. He said namaste and took his leave.

I went to Mrs Mukhopadhyay's house. She was a government doctor specializing in women's health and prenatal care. At the time I am speaking of, her husband had come from Bengal to be with her. I believe Mrs Mukhopadhyay was his second or third wife. They were blessed with one son and seven or eight daughters. A person seeing Mrs Mukhopadhyay and her daughters going for a bath in the Ganga would be reminded of 'Boys to Lilliput'. Mr Mukhopadhyay was the doubting sort. His suspicions lighted on any government official who came to visit the government lady doctor. The couple quarrelled frequently; old Mr Mukhopadhyay seldom got a full night's rest. The people with nothing better to do took sadistic pleasure in dropping in to visit them early in the morning.

I got to know them through a common friend who was a high-ranking Brahmin. He gave Mr Mukhopadhyay from Bengal the kind of regard that citizens of Bombay and Calcutta offer to non-metropolitan Indians. Mr Mukhopadhyay complained frequently about his domestic situation. On one such occasion, I asked him if he wanted to come to my house for a change and share a meal with me. Mr Mukhopadhyay accepted my invitation gladly. I was now counted among the regular visitors to his house. The government veterinarian, who was also Bengali, was another regular visitor. The Muslim Assistant Revenue Officer would also drop in. None of these people seemed impressed by Kulli. 'Kulli is doing such good work. Why don't you show some support for him?' I would ask.

'He is educating untouchable children for his own reasons,' they said. 'What he is looking for is a political base for himself. How much can he teach anyway? He is not too bright. All these Congress Party people are not too bright. And don't forget Kulli has gone ahead and brought a Muslim woman to live with him. He has had the purification rituals done in Ayodhya, he says. He even found a guru who breathed the initiation mantra into her ear. But a person doesn't become a scholar or teacher or reformer because someone breathes something into an ear. A person remains who he or she is. His woman wears tulsi beads around her neck. What hypocrisy!'

Kulli came two days later and escorted me to his school. There was a stretch of level ground in front of Kulli's house. Bamboo mats were laid out on the dirt. Eager students sat cross-legged on the mats. Trees grew in a hollow to one side, their leaves fluttering in the morning air. Kulli had the serene look of an ancient yogi in the forest. Some parents had heard I would be visiting the school. They came bearing small bouquets of flowers wrapped in leaves.

No one had treated these untouchables as equals for centuries. They had passed on to the other side, generation after generation, heads bowed low. There was no record of them in the world's history books. They could not say with pride that their ancestors composed the Ramayana or the Mahabharata. They could not say they were descended from King Ashoka or King Vikramaditya or King Harshavardhan or King Prithviraj. My mind clouded. I felt that what I had studied was worth nothing. What I had done was worth nothing. What I had dreamt of was worth nothing. Kulli was the true doer, the one lion among jackals. He was not well educated, but he transmitted sincerely everything he knew. The light of his sincerity shone in the faces of his pupils. My eyes held back tears.

Before I knew it, without hymn or ceremony, the unkempt tanners, street sweepers, washermen and toddy gatherers moved towards me. They laid their leaf-wrapped bouquets in front of me, afraid that if they touched me I would be defiled and would have to bathe again to become clean. My own civilization had made them lowly. They kept their heads bowed.

Kulli urged them forward. He told them I was one of them, that I sought their welfare, that I knew them to be equals. A current of happiness passed through them. Without cynicism they took me to be who Kulli said I was. I flushed from the purity of their intention. There was no room for cleverness here. My being a poet of God and beauty and splendour was worth nothing. My being a revolutionary was worth even less.

I composed myself. 'Please lay the bouquets in my hands the way brothers offer flowers to one another.' They smiled and came forward. The differences of bodies melted away. We were one spirit.

I did not stay long that day. After asking students a few questions about their exercises, I returned to the house of my in-laws.

Thirteen

Kulli visited me the following morning. 'I lost whatever social sympathy I enjoyed once I opened the school for untouchables. People seem keen on furthering their own advantage and not the least bit interested in allowing their neighbour a little opportunity. I understand well why India is a slave nation.'

'I ran into some government officials,' I told him. 'They were unhappy with your activities. Perhaps your work shows them up. Although they are servants of the government, they think they are the real power. Your activities remind them that human power vests in people like you.'

Kulli laughed. 'There's another problem. I live here. I am privy to what is going on. I know the inside stories and I share them with other people. The lady doctor in town is on the government payroll, but she charges a fee for attending to deliveries. I suggested to a pregnant washerwoman that she should call the doctor when she was in labour and not offer money. The washerwoman followed my counsel. The lady doctor was unhappy. The government veterinarian charges a fee for services that should be free. He is Muslim, and particularly unhappy that I have brought a Muslim woman to live with me. Doesn't he sing Ghalib's ghazal, '*Dil hi to hai na sango-khisht dard se bhar na aye kyon?*' (It's a heart, not a stone; why shouldn't it fill with pain?') Is it only Muslims who can feel for others? Are all Hindus faint of heart, mere traders who understand nothing beyond sacks of grain and monies receivable? I don't know what to do. I want to be accepted by others.'

'The Ganga that flows through you,' I responded, 'is the real Ganga. Literal-minded people think the Ganga is the river they see with their eyes. The untouchables will be purified in the Ganga you are directing towards them. But you should ask for some donations. How else will you manage?'

'They are very poor. I used to be a landlord. People still call me headman and think of me as a man of means. I can't ask my pupils for fees. I do ask them to bring me oil for the lamps at night. Night time is the only time older boys are free to come for lessons.'

'I have heard you performed ritual purification for your wife.'

'Yes,' Kulli admitted with a smile. 'I took her to Ayodhya and had her receive mantra from a guru. But Hindus aren't the accommodating sort. They said I had hung tulsi beads around a cat's neck and was now declaring the cat Hindu. The Maheshgiri ashram has promised a monthly contribution to the school. I approached Kunvar Sahib, who is chairman of the trust. He said I would receive money from them soon. But, in general, people are not favourably disposed to me.'

'Who are the people who stand in your way? I can talk to them.'

'It won't help,' Kulli said.

I repeated my request and Kulli named a few of those who were opposed.

'What do they have against you?'

'When I came back after my wife's purification, one of these worthies asked me which guru had breathed the sacred initiation in my wife's ear. I told them who the guru was. They sent a messenger to Ayodhya. He asked at the guru's ashram whether they knew what caste Kulli's wife was before initiating her. The guru's disciple made inquiries and answered they knew only that the woman was Kulli's wife. The messenger from Dalmau told them in Ayodhya that they had been deceived. The woman was Muslim. The news caused a sensation in the ashram. What would happen to donations if word of the initiation got around? The Babri Masjid matter had sharpened tension between Hindus and Muslims. Hindus claimed the Muslim mosque had been built on top of the birthplace of Lord Ram. Things could get out of control at any time. "You can go back to your town," the disciple told the messenger. "We will take care of the man who deceived us." The messenger came back to Dalmau. I received a letter in the mail. "You deceived us. Return the sacred beads and mantra to us. Otherwise, we will reverse the effect of the initiation through our spiritual powers. You may come to harm."'

'So you don't have any rights in the matter?'

'I have all the rights any living person has, and in any case I don't believe in these rituals, but those who do believe must abide by the guru's instructions. I did as they said.'

'Did you express your view on the subject?'

'I did, and the guru had nothing to say. You are a hypocrite

if you can't accept a Muslim woman who asks for the mantra.
There is no spirituality in your work, only commerce. You
can reverse the initiation as much as you like. Your threats
are useless. Hindus have tricked society for a long time,
but they will not prevail against this woman. She is made
of the same stuff as Kabir. She has faith in the God in her
heart. This is how sage Ramanand spoke as he accepted the
Muslim Kabir as his disciple. And because of that initiation,
a thousand gurus like you became Kabir's disciples. He led
Hindus round in a circle. He led Muslims round in a circle.
He was a first class idiot.' Kulli said vehemently.

'Did you write to Mahatma Gandhi?' I asked.

'He must be a hypocrite like the others,' Kulli said.

'Maybe not,' I replied. 'He has committed an entire year
to untouchability reform. He is planning a reform tour from
one corner of the country to the other.'

'Touring is all we will get. What work will he do? He
never thought about untouchables earlier. Now that the
government is after him, he wants to escape by promoting
social reform.'

'Aren't you engaged in social reform, too, my friend?'

'I am not working for any organization,' Kulli said angrily.
'If Mahatma Gandhi believes in social reform let him a marry
a Muslim woman and bring her home to live with him.'

'What sort of a person are you? He is too old to bring a
woman home.'

'That's true,' Kulli said. Perhaps he was contemplating
the letter he would write.

'How can I find a way? There is no help in sight and yet
the work must be done.'

'The direction great men take marks out the path,' I replied. 'Keep walking the way you are going. You will meet others more famous than you on the path. Join them. That's how it works. Each one of us uses the materials available in our time. We observe how others use the material. We learn from them and then make our own contribution. If you want to improve conditions for untouchable people, meet those who pursue similar goals. If they are deceiving others, there is nothing you can do about it. You need to keep moving forward. Mahatma Gandhi is respected by the great ones of the world. He is no ordinary person.'

Kulli fell silent. 'We lack the presence of the Congress Party. We are a good-sized town, but people here laugh at the idea of an independent nation. We need to bring the Congress Party here.'

A fire blazed, and from within Kulli the true man appeared. There is no man greater than such a person. He can raise his voice against the Almighty if necessary. He measures good and evil by his own standards. Fame has nothing to do with such greatness.

I was watching Kulli intently. 'The tanner Madhua's wife is running a fever. She is in a bad way. I will take her to the hospital if I can. Otherwise I will beg the doctor to make a charity call. How can they possibly come up with money for his fees? She is alone at home. Madhua is at work, and their son is out grazing cattle.' Kulli left in a hurry.

I got up to go and meet the members of the Maheshgiri ashram management committee. The members of such committees are reputable citizens, which means they are constantly threatened by the disreputable things going on around them. Lalaji was the first committee member I ran into. He was at a tailor's shop waiting for a coat to be fitted. I knew him well. He owned a little land and was quite the dresser. His tailor told me in Lalaji's presence that he would not have moved his tailor shop from Rae Bareli to Dalmau if it were not for Lalaji. Lalaji was particular about the correct measurement of individual limbs and particular about the fitting. An artisan is drawn to patrons who require fine work.

Lalaji said namaste when he saw me; the tailor did likewise. I am not one to mumble automatic benediction upon those who join their palms to greet me. Usually I grin foolishly. My young son asked me once why I never conferred blessings on those who bowed to me. I told him I was not in the habit—that I hadn't picked up the formalities of behaving my son had learned from my in-laws.

'So what do you want?' Lalaji asked boisterously.

'I hear you are a member of the Maheshgiri ashram management committee. People think well of you. You are my friend; I think well of you, too. But there is a little matter I would like to discuss privately.'

Lalaji led the way out. The tailor eyed us with the detachment of a literary critic. When we were alone, I spoke words of prose in my best poetic manner. 'Have a care for the untouchables,' I said.

'I see Kulli has spoken to you and you being a simple person imagine things are the way he described them. I would advise you not to get into this.'

'I am used to things not being the way people describe them. I practise literary irony myself.'

'What kind of irony?'

'For example, you have a head on your shoulders. But it may not be an ordinary head. It may have horns growing out of it.'

'Which means...?'

'I don't know what it means.'

'Tell me what you want.'

Now he is coming around, I thought to myself. Time to have some fun. 'I overheard a group of people as I was walking home,' I said to him. 'They were saying, "Lalaji should be taught a lesson. We might need to break a bone or two. He is at the tailor's all the time."'

'Did they give a reason for their hostility?'

'I wouldn't know. They were dark-skinned people, probably tanners or toddy gatherers.'

'Have you seen Kulli recently?'

'Not for a while. I kept trying to understand why those people on the road were unhappy with you.'

Lalaji returned to the tailor shop. I made my way to the Pandit's house. It must have been eleven in the morning. The Pandit was flying one of those square kites. He had ordered special string paste from Lucknow to keep other kite flyers from bringing down his kite.

'I have come on important business,' I said.

'Can't you see I am busy?'

I realized he would be a difficult case. 'The Deputy Collector is down from Rae Bareli. He wanted a bath in the Ganga. He knew I would be here; I met him when I visited Rae Bareli recently.'

'Where is he now?' the Pandit asked eagerly.

'At my house. He wanted to see you. He would have accompanied me, but I advised against it. "You have just bathed," I said. "You will get hot in the sun. It's a climb to the Pandit's house. The Pandit is my friend. I will ask him to come see you here."'

The Pandit handed the kite to a servant and instructed him to wind the string on a spool. 'Hurry up and wind the string,' the Pandit shouted, 'I am going out to meet the Deputy Collector.'

He put on a fresh kurta and picked up his walking stick. I marvelled at his brisk pace as we walked. We were half way to my house when he paused and asked me if I knew Mahadev Prasad.

'Yes,' I said. 'What about him?' He did not answer; he was absorbed in his own thoughts.

I opened the door to my sitting room. 'Where is the Deputy Collector?'

'He may have gotten impatient and left.'

'You tricked me,' the Pandit said.

'It's not as if you dealt with me generously. You are a pandit, but you've never imparted any wisdom to me.'

'I have nothing to say to people like you,' the Pandit answered angrily.

I realized then that the Pandit's upper storey was empty— no learning there, no wisdom. 'My coming to your house was as pointless as your coming to mine,' I said. 'Please go home and resume flying kites.'

Fourteen

I had to spend some time in Lucknow. When I returned to Dalmau, I was eager to know whether Kulli's work had moved forward. I heard his praises right inside my in-laws' house. My brother-in-law's wife had taken over the running of the household in place of my wife. She was already the mother of three children; it was permissible for me to engage her in conversation. From behind her veil, she responded gladly to talk about literature.

I reminded her that Mahatma Gandhi was against the veil. It was not becoming of a disciple of the great man to be wearing a veil while conversing with me. 'I don't like the veil,' she said, 'but the men here read meanings into everything.'

'So you want to pull a veil over their eyes by covering your own,' I remarked.

My mother-in-law and my brother-in-law's young wife wanted to talk about nothing but Kulli's work. 'He is a good man,' they claimed, 'performing important service. At first people would assemble and spend their time criticizing one another. Now they cooperate. The Congress Party has a base in the town. There is a strong core of volunteers. All this is Kulli's doing.'

'He works eighteen hours a day,' my brother-in-law added. 'He will walk ten miles to add a new member to the Congress Party rolls. People respect him. They get up from their seats when he enters a room.'

'He is superhuman,' Mother-in-law said.

My brother-in-law's wife concurred. 'He is an avatar. The tanner Binda's bride lay dying. Nobody stepped forward to help. Only Kulli went to sit by her side and look to her needs.'

'I have to see him,' I said. I was eager to know how Mahatma Gandhi replied to the letter Kulli must have sent him.

My brother-in-law said he would let Kulli know. He got his walking stick, cast a quick glance at his wife and at me, then a longer trusting glance at his mother. I made my way to the sitting room.

I was beginning to be recognized. Students from nearby schools and colleges often dropped in and I had to make time for them. They would ask me what chhayavaad poetry was. I had gotten used to explaining, but the students couldn't understand. I would assure them that they would understand by and by.

I also made the acquaintance of Babu Iqbal Varma Sehar at this time. He had sought me out on account of his interest in literature. I was delighted to discover that his in-laws and mine dwelt in the same town. He brought along a friend who was the brother of Babu Rajbahadur Lamgora, the famous scholar and critic of Tulsidas. I admired Babu Lamgora's criticism and had long wanted to meet him, but there had been no opportunity. I mentioned this to Babu Lamgora's brother who invited me to their house in Fatehpur. Babu Sehar asked me to recite my poetry, which I was happy to do. There were other occasions, too, in which poetry recitation was involved, but we can let those pass. The listeners associated with these occasions were not newsworthy. I noticed, incidentally, that people were puzzled upon reading my poems but understood them perfectly when they heard them recited.

I was absorbed in searching out new feelings to write about when my brother-in-law returned. 'Here is Kulli,' he said, showing him in. I greeted Kulli and he sat down beside me. My brother-in-law went to his own rooms. Kulli's face looked bright, but his body was emaciated as of a person in the evening of his life. I felt stangely elated at the contrast between his failing body and his glowing presence.

He sat without moving. I had never seen him this quiet before. I sensed he was on an interior journey, having shown the world the path to follow. I, too, sat quiet.

Kulli sighed. I believe his sigh was for those who were unsuspecting. The simple-hearted people suffered the most. Those dedicated to the seva of society served their own interests as well. Many peasants joined the Congress Party for protection from landlords and moneylenders. Even poor people sang the praises of those who could do something for them. Was self-interest the only motivation at work in society? Could such motivation bring peace to the soul?

He was so quiet I didn't have the courage to begin a conversation. Just then my brother-in-law appeared with a tray of snacks. 'Kulli has been looking after the tanner

Dukhiya all night. Dukhiya's wife is dead and Dukhiya has taken ill. He is on his way to Lalganj on Congress Party work. I don't think he has had a meal since lunch yesterday.'

Kulli picked up the plate of snacks and began to eat. His face was flushed. I bowed inwardly before the humanity that had taken root in him.

He ate rapidly, rinsed his mouth and picked up a fold of paan. My brother-in-law left.

'Kulli,' I said mustering my courage, 'did you write that letter to Mahatma Gandhi?'

Kulli smiled. 'What can I say?' he responded.

His smile was enough. I got up and walked from one end of the sitting room to another. The time for role playing was over. 'It makes me angry. Why can't the great ones tell genuine people from hypocrites? Once a few social workers deceive them, they imagine all social workers are imposters.' Kulli showed interest. 'This is why I stay away from politics,' I continued. 'I know I can never be the president of the provincial Congress committee. 'The dharma of a foot soldier,' they will say to me, 'is not to aspire to be leader.' The leaders, meanwhile, will pursue every stratagem to stay leaders. They won't let others climb up.' Kulli was stirred by my words.

'What answer did you receive from Mahatma Gandhi?'

'None. I addressed seventeen letters to him. Or was it twenty-seven? I can't remember. Mahatma Gandhi remained true to his vow of silence. I believe Mahadev Desai scrawled a sentence in reply to one of my letters: 'Write to the provincial office of the party in Allahabad.'

'Didn't you answer back?'

Kulli cleared his throat. 'I did. "You may be a thousand times more educated than me," I wrote to Mahatma Gandhi. "You may be world famous. That does not mean you know about every kind of situation people face. If you knew about these situations you could never take a vow of silence. Because you are silent I know there is nothing divine about you. God is omniscient. You are not. Avatars have been born into other castes, but not to traders. Therefore traders have deified you, and you have happily become a deity looking out for traders."'

'Did you write anything of substance in your letter?'

'Seventeen times in the earlier letters.'

'Was this the eighteenth or the twenty-eighth?'

'I don't remember. You can see my copies when you come to the house.'

'Did you include any lines of verse in your letter? These add to the effect.'

'I didn't think of it. I wrote directly whatever came to mind. I know I am not well educated. They can think me foolish if they like. But God does not distinguish between the learned and the ignorant. He regards both with an equal eye.'

'Mahatma Gandhi isn't that kind of god.'

'What did you do next?'

'I sent a letter to Allahabad (I can't remember the name of the office of untouchable affairs to which Kulli addressed his letter), but I received no reply. So I wrote to Jawaharlal Nehru.'

'What did you say?'

'I wrote a straightforward letter at first,' Kulli said gravely, 'such as we write to important people. But after not hearing from him, I wrote in a sharper tone. I had nothing to lose.'

'You were writing to the king himself.'

'Yes, to the king. He didn't reply to the second letter directly, but he had it sent over to the office of untouchable affairs. They wrote to me saying they would help. Money intended for me would be sent to the Rae Bareli office.'

'Did you get any money?'

'Only once,' Kulli said, staring out the window. 'The great ones know why they act as they do. I don't want to say much. I am also learning to see my own fault in such things. I wasn't satisfied the way one is satisfied with a simple meal of rotis and dal. I must leave for Lalganj now. I am trying to enroll new members in the Congress Party. There is so much work to be done. My wife has taken over running the school. I would be happy if you visited the school again. I am going to be away for many days. There is no one else to help me. I have left things to God. Don't mind my whirling words. Namaste.'

He may have grown older, but there was vigour in his stride. He had turned his face to God only because he lacked for human help, human support, human encouragement.

Fifteen

I stayed in Dalmau another two or three days. I visited Kulli's wife and saw his school. Then I left for Lucknow. But I didn't like it there. Something kept pulling me back to Dalmau. Scenes of Dalmau's natural beauty would appear in my mind—the flow of the Ganga, the open riverbanks, the wide horizons. The strongest attraction was to Kulli. I could hear his affection calling out to me: Come back to Dalmau, come back. I needed to bathe in the Ganga for the kakti festival, I reminded myself. Barely three months had elapsed before I found myself back in Dalmau.

The banks of the river glowed with autumn light. The trees were washed by the rains. Everywhere there was clarity and radiance. I was riding in a trap such as I had ridden many years ago when I first met Kulli. How that fashionable revenue stamp salesman had changed. He had moved into the circle of light.

The trap stopped in front of the house of my in-laws. A man came out to help unload the luggage. Mother-in-law watched from the gate. She had the cart driver paid at once. I touched her feet and went inside. My brother-in-law's wife came to the door. She was wearing a sari, no other upper garment, no veil. I found myself bowing before her natural beauty.

I have stumbled many times in my life, but I also know our stumbles enable us to penetrate the veil. My brother-in-law emerged from an inner room. 'You have come at the right time,' he said to me. 'Kulli is very sick. The doctor says the case is hopeless, but they may have instruments and medicines in Rae Bareli that could save him. Try to see him soon.'

'What is he ill with?'

'Venereal disease,' my brother-in-law said. 'He had contracted it earlier, but he pushed himself running from village to village in the heat, signing up members for the Congress Party. There isn't a village in the area now without party members. He would go days without food. His health failed him. His lower limbs have rotted. There is a terrible stench and strangely...'

'Strangely?'

My brother-in-law smiled.

'What's there to smile about?'

My brother-in-law glanced at his mother and wife standing nearby, and motioned me to another part of the room. He whispered in my ear: 'The genital organ is missing.'

'Missing?'

'It wasted away, that's what people say. Even if he survives, they say, what use will he be to his wife?'

I sat down at the edge of the bed. My brother-in-law's wife said gravely, 'He isn't doing well at all.'

Mother-in-law went in to prepare breakfast and called my brother-in-law's wife into the kitchen to help. I sat stupefied. The talk over breakfast pertained to matters concerning our family.

I set out for Kulli's house the following morning. I met some Congress Party social workers on my way who were also headed to see him. I saw a group of untouchable children and a few parents by his door. Their eyes were despairing.

I found Kulli in the same position in which I had seen him that first day. Those disturbed feelings had worked themselves out in his body; they were not present in his face. His face shone with light. At the same time, the stench was unbearable; I had to force myself to stay in the room. Kulli opened his eyes, 'Ah, it's you,' he said. 'How fortunate I am.' He asked one of the untouchable people in the room to spread a small rug near his pillow. 'If you sit at the head of the bed,' he said, 'the smell will not bother you. I have confined the disease to the nether parts. Above my heart, I am well. See for yourself.'

I sat at the head of the bed. It was true there was no stench there. I took out a five-rupee note and gave it to Kulli's wife; he would need milk. Kulli gazed at the ceiling and said nothing.

'What does the doctor say?' I asked.

'There is nothing left to say. It's up to God now.' Kulli closed his eyes.

I sat in the room a little longer. Kulli's wife began to cry when I prepared to leave. 'They say I should take him to Rae Bareli. It will cost these five rupees. He doesn't want to be carried in a palanquin. If we can find a truck that's unloading in Dalmau and going back empty I can transport him to the hospital, but how will we deal with the expenses once we get there?'

'Please take him to the hospital. I will raise money for his treatment and meet you in Rae Bareli.'

She looked at me with gratitude. I took my leave.

Word reached my in-laws the next day that Kulli's wife had found a suitable truck and taken him to Rae Bareli. I had to start collecting money. I asked a few local social workers to accompany me and went to meet the president of the Congress committee in Dalmau. The president was busy overseeing the construction of his brick house, one of whose already finished rooms constituted the party office. The social workers introduced me; the president was familiar with Kulli's work. When I mentioned money the president said making a contribution would be against party rules. 'The party collects money from members but does not pay money out to members.'

'I know the rule. I also know that when the party considers a member worthy, it makes funds available in such a way that no one ever finds out.'

'What do you mean?'

'I have told you what I had to say.'

'No money will be given for Kulli's care,' he declared with presidential authority.

'I have already contributed five rupees,' I said. 'I can add two rupees more. I will bear the expenses they will incur in Rae Bareli. Providing more than this is beyond my powers. Three of my friends have given me one rupee each. If you give us a little money we will be able to manage.'

'There were seven rupees left from the sum allocated for

a reception for Vijayalakshami[15]. It turns out she did not pay us a visit; the funds have been returned to the party coffers.'

'You know that Kulli's life is more precious than a reception for Vijayalakshami.'

'These sticklers for rules say I have extended my property line two yards into municipal land.'

Is that why you are eager to hobnob with Vijayalakshami? I thought to myself. But out loud I said, 'Whenever someone arranges a reception for Vijayalakshami she finds out if an ulterior motive might be at work. If the reception is not as innocent as it seems she goes after the perpetrator with a vengeance. She is Goddess Kali incarnate.' I joined my palms in namaste, taking leave of him. 'She keeps her distance from everyone; she does not invite visitors to her house. But if she learns that a Congress Committee has invested money in the care of its own workers, she is happy to support that committee in every way.'

'Do you see her frequently?'

'She doesn't see people casually, but if I have work with her she does not refuse a meeting. A real Goddess Kali.'

'You can have those seven rupees.'

'Thank you.'

I took the money and prepared to go to Rae Bareli. One of Kulli's Muslim friends met me at the train station. He, too, was going to visit Kulli. When we arrived at the hospital the doctor informed us that Kulli's condition had improved. 'Earlier he was screaming with pain. He is better now.' However, upon seeing Kulli, I had the opposite impression. The operation

[15] Minister of local self-government in UP, 1937–39. Sister of Jawaharlal Nehru.

had made him weaker. He seemed withdrawn. 'The doctors here know nothing,' Kulli said. 'I tell them that I only have a few hours left. I ask them to stop giving me false hope. They tell me I am mistaken—that I will be up and about soon.'

Kulli was calm. I could detect no hesitation in his words or in the expression on his face. The doctor looked in while I was present. 'Please allow people to visit me. I don't have much time left. There is no reason to send out people to get fruit or milk.'

'If you had direct knowledge of your condition, you shouldn't have come to the hospital in the first place. Now that you have been admitted, do as we say. There was rattling in your throat when you got here. The rattling is gone.'

'It wasn't in my throat,' Kulli said. 'It was my breathing through the nose that was noisy. I am weaker now. There's less breathing through the nose.'

'Be quiet. Are you telling me we doctors can't distinguish between throat and nose?'

The doctor moved on to the next patient. Kulli followed him calmly with his eyes.

I had heard in Dalmau that Kulli's wife didn't have a moment of rest when his condition worsened. She was busy running errands in Rae Bareli.

I wanted to understand things clearly.

'Is she beside herself with grief?' I asked.

I couldn't get a definite answer.

Unfortunately, she wasn't at the hospital when I visited. When I couldn't stay any longer I told Kulli I had brought some money for his medical care. I had hoped to hand the funds over to his wife.

'You can leave the money with him,' Kulli said, pointing to the Muslim gentleman. 'My wife has been busy with one thing after another.'

I gave the rupees to the Muslim gentleman.

Kulli asked me where I would spend the night. I told him the Treasury Officer in town was a friend. I would stay at his bungalow and inform him about Kulli's condition. I wanted to collect money for Kulli in Rae Bareli as well.

I joined my palms in namaste. Tears rolled down Kulli's eyes. 'We won't meet again,' he said.

Sixteen

I brought Kulli's condition to the attention of the Treasury Officer and returned to Dalmau. I received a message two days later saying Kulli had died, and that his corpse was being transported to Dalmau. Social workers, untouchables in Dalmau, and members of the Congress Party set about organizing a funeral procession to the river. A boat was to carry the body across to the burning ground on the other side. Since Kulli's wife was not wedded to him in the proper way, she would not be allowed to light the pyre. A distant relative of Kulli's had been summoned for the purpose. I was stunned by these events. I would never behold Kulli again. But I was also amazed at the outpouring of grief. How had this ordinary man come to matter so much? I won't cheapen words by writing down what Kulli thought of me, but I do know which person's example made the deepest impression on him. In their last days, Premchand and Jaishankar Prasad shared some confidences of their lives with me. I will keep their secrets safe. Making them public would only stir gossip and cause pain to the departed souls. Kulli, too, lived with a secret. Premchand and Jaishankar Prasad parted with their secret late. They were concerned for their reputation. Kulli parted with his secret early.

When I learn of the passing of a dear person or fear their demise, I fall into a kind of stupor. I was in the sitting room when I heard Kulli was dead. I was in the sitting room when I was told his corpse had arrived in Dalmau. A social worker came to summon me two or three times. I was in the sitting room when the funeral procession set out. I said I was unable to join. People cremated him and returned. I was seated as before. That evening I ate my dinner as usual. Kulli's wife sobbed and cried. I heard her but did nothing. Ten days passed.

On the eleventh day—but I was unaware that it was the ritual eleventh day after cremation—I went and met Kulli's wife. 'Kulli is gone,' she said. 'His work here is over. But what about the people who came to mourn the first ten days after his cremation and won't come today—is their work over? Does their absence prove their Hindu purity or their Hindu duplicity?'

I told her I didn't understand. 'Can you speak more clearly?'

'All right,' she began, the way a preacher begins a sermon. 'You weren't present, but somebody touched a torch to his funeral pyre. I don't know who it was; I believe he is a distant relative. We mourned him for ten days. The priest and a large number of townspeople were present on the tenth day. The distant relative said he had to leave for his village to look after an ailing uncle. What if something happened to the uncle? He was his only living relative. The distant relative told me I could make the eleventh day's funeral offering myself. The priest assented. The circle of people around him assented. "You can make the funeral offering yourself." Today is the eleventh day and I sent for the priest. But he refused to come.'

'Why did he refuse?'

The boy who went to call the priest was an untouchable. He came back with the following report: 'Pandit Manni complains that life is difficult enough for him because he is priest to mixed caste Gangaputras. No one will marry the Pandit's sister for this reason. If he comes to your house to make the eleventh day offering, no one will share food or drink with him any more.'

'Do you hear what he says?' Kulli's wife asked me. 'If he didn't intend to go through with the ceremony why did Pandit Manni ask me to initiate it? There were ten witnesses: Pandit Ramgulam, Rajaram Gangaputra, Dhokhe Mahabahman...'

'We are not in a court of law,' I responded. 'We can't force the Pandit to come.'

I knew Pandit Manni. He was from the high Kanyakubja caste of Brahmins. No one had sought his sister's hand in marriage—she was going on twenty—because he served castes much lower than his own. The Pandit had no other skills; performing rituals was the only way he could make a living.

'Don't worry,' I said to Kulli's wife. 'Your work will be done.'

'Only if people like you take an interest...' she said with exaggerated sadness. She ran the end of her sari over her eyes as if to wipe them. 'Only if you go and summon him yourself...'

'I understand,' I said. 'But it's not at Pandit Manni's house where my presence is needed. It is needed here. I will go home and bathe. Send for the Pandit one more time. I should be back very soon. I will conduct the eleventh day ceremony myself if the Pandit does not appear.' Kulli's wife looked at me as if I was the sage Vasishtha, promising to add glory to the funerary rites at her house.

I walked back towards my in-laws' house. The astrologer who inspected horoscopes for my wedding lived on the road that led to my in-laws. He indicated that marrying me would be inauspicious. My father-in-law wanted to refuse the match being proposed. But the astrologer's father, who was regarded as a master astrologer, overruled his son. 'The match is fine,' the old astrologer declared. 'Even if misfortune befalls them, the harm to the woman will not be great. Besides, if the young man's horoscope shows him to be unfortunate, the young woman's horoscope shows her to be a demoness. They are well matched. They will manage all right.' Since that time, I have held the astrologer's family in special regard.

The astrologer was older than I am. I joined my palms in respectful greeting and asked him how the stars were aligned that day. Was the day auspicious for ritual events? The astrologer was puzzled. He knew the sort of person I was. 'Why would the alignment of stars make a difference to you?' he wondered. I explained that Pandit Manni was reluctant to officiate at Kulli's house. The Pandit was worried about how his service to clients of doubtful caste might reflect on marriage prospects for his sister. I was planning to conduct the eleventh day ceremony myself.

'The astrological names of day and year are needed for the sacred mantras.'

'Do you know anything about making oblations with ghee?'

'I don't, but I understand that all the spiritual powers are invoked in the offering, from Brahma to gods and demons, to humans and kinnars. I can add some thoughts of my own in Sanskrit. My conjugation of verbs will be superior to what local priests utter.'

'That is so.'

'Let me borrow your almanac,' I said. 'Time is short.'

I arrived at my in-laws' house bearing the almanac. Mother-in-law was more surprised than she would have been seeing me walk in wearing shoes on my head. 'What do you have there?' she asked.

'The almanac,' I answered. 'Please request a bucket of fresh water for me. I need to bathe quickly.'

'What are you up to?'

'Pandit Manni is unable to officiate at Kulli's eleventh day ceremony. He is worried that his service to mixed caste Brahmins has already discredited him. If he goes to Kulli's house his respectability will suffer irreparably and he will be unable to get his sister married.' I set the almanac to one side and began undressing for my bath.

Mother-in-law had her doubts. 'What do you know about the ritual?'

'I know enough.'

'You will serve as the officiating priest?'

'Please have a twist of sacred thread laid out.'

'You will bring our family to ruin.'

'Why is that?'

'People will stop sharing food and water with us.'

'I am not a blood relative. There is no reason for you to endure ostracism for my sins. All you may be required to do is forbid me entry to the kitchen and serve me my food outside.'

Mother-in-law began to sob. I bathed and put on the sacred thread. 'People here know I don't wear the sacred thread. If they had wanted to ostracize you they could have found an excuse a lot sooner. I am well acquainted with those hypocrites.'

I was about to leave when Mother-in-law thought about food. 'Eat before you go.'

'No,' I said. 'I will eat on my return.'

'You will have eaten food from their kitchen by the time you come back. Bahu,' she called out, 'serve him food.'

I ate quickly and set out. A throng of people was moving towards Kulli's house. I had gained something of a reputation by 1937. I had turned forty-one and grown venerable. There was general amazement that it was I who would perform the eleventh day ceremony for Kulli.

Not everyone could fit into Kulli's courtyard. Many attendees wanted to find out whether I could conduct the ceremony competently. Some had doubts. Others sensed my confidence and were reassured. Kulli's wife looked at me with gratitude. My arrival had already saved her from public embarrassment.

I sat down in the courtyard at the appropriate time. Kulli's wife sat opposite. Some people sat, the others stood. Some

were able to get in, others stood outside. I began drawing
the sacred diagram. I drew a large square such as children
make playing surbaggha. I knew enough to make nine
houses for the nine planets. I spread some sand for an altar,
upon which I laid chips of wood. I painted the auspicious
svastika sign on a clay water pot. I placed a coconut in front
and lit a lamp atop the water pot.

My recitation of the mantras was unsteady; I couldn't find
the right pandit voice. I tried to exercise my imagination. I
imagined I was living in the sixteenth century at the time of
Surdas and Tulsidas. I imagined myself reading their poetry
out loud. My face grew calmer. My recitation improved.
Then I launched into Sanskrit, singing the praises of Lord
Ganesha and Gauri. The listeners settled down and became
lost in thought as sometimes happens at poetry festivals.
After praying, I began the ceremony of pouring ghee on
wood chips and invoking individual gods. I don't know
what gods I called upon, but I would pronounce a name
and Kulli's wife would repeat the name after me. The people
present were convinced the ritual was right.

At the end of the ceremony, I directed Kulli's wife to
practise a year of abstinence in honour of her husband. I
instructed her in this vow in Sanskrit. Most of those present
could make out the Sanskrit words for 'I, Kulli's devoted
wife.' They smiled indulgently and this was the smile with
which the ceremony of funeral offerings ended.

'It went well for her,' I heard a critic say as I was leaving. 'She
has been declared Kulli's wife.' I said nothing and continued
on the way to my in-law's.

Ritual flour and ghee for the officiating priest were sent over from Kulli's house later that evening. 'Please set these aside for me,' I told Mother-in-law. 'You can use flour and ghee to make pooris for me tomorrow.'

'They have sent enough for several meals. There is no way you could use that much ghee for one batch of pooris.'

The next day, as was my usual practice, I bought some mutton from the butcher.

'You said you were going to eat pooris,' my mother-in-law remarked.

'Kulli's wife was a meat-eating Muslim before she was Kulli's wife. I felt it was appropriate to align myself with her old customs. There is no fault in such things.'

P.S.

Bhavbhay Darunam:
Terror of Being
Satti Khanna

⊷⊜ ⊜⊶

Insights
Interviews
& More...

Suryakant Tripathi 'Nirala' had turned forty-one when he composed the eponymous autobiographical accolade to Kulli Bhaat (*A Life Misspent*). He was residing in Lucknow at the time, cobbling a living from copy-editing and proofreading, and from small payments for original poems and essays. He had gained something of a reputation, as he says. His dense existential poetry had dynamized Hindi letters. He was a hero to many young poets and critics. And yet he was living hand to mouth, making futile attempts to solve crossword puzzles in *Saraswati* in hopes of winning the much needed prize money.[1]

His elegy, *Saroj Smriti*, on the untimely death of his daughter Saroj, offers glimpses of the dire poverty in which Nirala maintained his sense of purpose. The poem is a lament for the privations he unwittingly inflicted upon his daughter. At the same time, in restraint and simplicity, it is unbearably beautiful:

[1] Sharma, Ramvilas. *Nirala ki Sahitya Sadhana.* New Delhi: Rajkamal Prakashan, 1990. (1: 303).

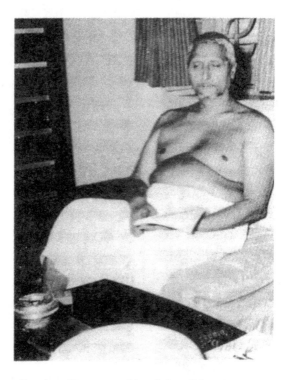

Daughter, I was a worthless father, did
nothing for you. Although I knew some ways
of earning, I would always let them slip
away, knowing as I well knew the wrongs
attending the path to wealth. I always lost
the struggle for success. And so, my dear,
I couldn't dress you in silk or even give you
enough to eat. But I could never snatch
the poor man's bread or bear to see him weep.
In my tears I always saw reflected
only my own face and my own heart.[2]

[2] Nirala, Suryakant Tripathi. *A Season on Earth*. Trans. David Rubin. New York: Columbia University Press, 1976. (89).

Nirala was born in Mahishadal, a hundred miles south of Calcutta, on Basant Panchami, 1896.[3] His family hailed from the Baiswara region of Uttar Pradesh, a region well known for its hardy peasant stock. Many farming families supplied broad-

---

[3] Basant Panchami fell on Sunday, January 19, that year.

chested soldiers to the Indian army. When the princely estate of Mahishadal passed from a Bengali raja to a raja from Baiswara, opportunity opened up for young men from Baiswara to serve the Raja of Mahishadal. The new raja wanted a security detail from among his own people. Nirala's father, Ramsahay Tripathi, found employment as a member of the raja's 'army', seven hundred miles away from his ancestral village of Garhakola in Uttar Pradesh.

The 'army' was quartered in mud and thatch houses some distance—across ponds and orchards—from the stately palace of the raja. Nirala grew up fluent in the local language of Bengali, but his schooling was interrupted by family visits to Garhakola, and later, by the customary early marriage. He never graduated from high school.

He was married at the age of twelve to a girl a year younger than he was. They began living together when he was sixteen. His wife and many members of his extended family died six years later in the influenza pandemic of 1918. Nirala's mother had died when he was three. His father had passed away in 1917. Nirala was, in many ways, alone in the world, having four nephews, a four-year-old son, and year-old Saroj to look after.

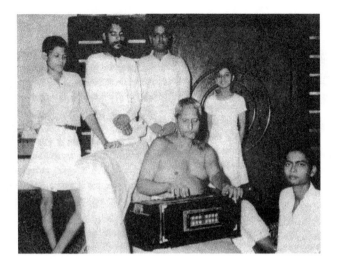

Of me so long unlucky you
had been the one blessing. Deprived of you
… life remains
one tale of woe.[4]

In consideration of Nirala's father's service, the Raja of
Mahishadal offered Nirala work as scribe and accountant. *A
Life Misspent* informs us how this spell of employment ended.
Nirala returned to Garhakola in 1921 and looked for work with
publishers and literary magazines. Prospective employers paid little
attention to his self-education in Hindi, Sanskrit and Bengali.
The lack of academic degrees proved to be a signal disadvantage.
He elected to go back to Bengal later that year when the Raja of
Mahishadal repeated a request for his services.

He stayed in Mahishadal only a few months. Through his
interest in Ramakrishna Parmahansa, Nirala had come in contact

---

[4] *A Season on Earth* (95).

with publishers of the spiritual magazine *Samanvay* in Calcutta. He was happy to move in with the sannyasis and edit *Samanvay* without any arrangements about salary; the legal and accounting work in Mahishadal had become meaningless.

Once in Calcutta, Nirala made the acquaintance of Mahadev Prasad Seth, owner of Balkrishna Press and printer of *Samanvay* magazine. Mahadev Prasad wanted to start a humor magazine in Hindi, and found in Nirala and two other associates a core group sufficient for the purpose. They called the magazine *Matwala* (The Intoxicated One) and filled it with poems and commentary written under assumed names to suggest a much larger staff. One of the assumed names Nirala used in the magazine stuck. He had previously been known only by his family name of Suryakant Tripathi. Now the pen name was added to the family name.

Henceforth, he was Suryakant Tripathi 'Nirala'. Nirala shared lodgings with Mahadev Prasad Seth and the two associates, but again there were no arrangements about salary. Mahadev Prasad Seth was host; the associate writers for his magazine were welcome guests.

Nirala wrote poetry for *Matwala* in the Khari Boli his wife introduced him to. He chose to write in blank verse, relying for evocative power on the beat of words rather than on end-rhyme. His poems challenged the decorousness of courtly poetry in the Braj language of Mathura, which dominated Hindi poetry at the time.

By his own example, Nirala wanted to strengthen Khari Boli so it would be adequate to the philosophic and aesthetic needs of the new nation. He felt that great leaders such as Gandhi and Nehru lacked acquaintance with the depth of Hindi literature and with the vigour of Nirala's own practice. He had

opportunity to meet them both and to try to convince them of the great progress Hindi had made. Some of the satire directed at them in *A Life Misspent* may derive from Nirala's failure to persuade either Gandhi or Nehru in this regard.

A poem of Nirala's published in *Matwala* indicates the romanticism which acquired the name of Chhayavad (shadowiness). It is an early poem, born of word music and deep receptivity to nature. It hints at but does not undertake the existential inquiry Nirala's mature creativity was to make. In *Sandhya Sundari*[5] (Evening) the poet's heart aches for the loveliness of the evening. It aches also because the weary are lulled. They are soothed to forgetfulness; the conditions that bring on weariness haven't changed.

---

[5] Nirala, Suryakant Tripathi. *Rachanavali*. 2nd ed. New Delhi: Rajkamal Prakashan, 1998. (1: 77–78).

Day's dying–
Gathering clouds–
In gauze like angel's wings
Evening slowly, very slowly,
Comes below.
Red lips and
Somber darkness.
A single star pinned to her raven hair
Marks her as queen.

Arms round her girl friend silence
On undulating umber path
Soft bud on vine–

No trembling of sitar strings from her touch,
No tintinnabulation from her feet,
Only her finger at her lips: Hush! Hush!
Hush! Hush! Like thoughts before they find a form.
Hush! To the stream, hush! To the mountain top,
Hush! To the turbulence of ocean waves,
Hush! Hush! The fire and the flowing air.

She draws the weary
Stroking face and hair
Pouring dark wine for sweet forgetfulness
Merging into the stillness of the night.

Restless and ardent
From the poet's throat
A song breaks forth–
Raga of endless aching.[6]

A Life Misspent, in contrast, is a mature work. It brings *bhavbhay darunam* (terror of being) into consideration.

[6] Translation mine.

The tone is ironic. The movement from scene to scene is often abrupt. Nirala's despair when he returns to Dalmau is left to the imagination. The novel breaks off without leave-taking. The concision of the prose reminds one of Dante's Francesca: 'A Galeotto was the book and he that wrote it; that day we read in it no further.'[7]

When Nirala encountered opposition to his 'rough' style, he said he suffered from being an outsider. Had he been born to a princely family, he said, his innovations would have been celebrated as Rabindranth's were in Bengal. He was right that better credentials would have eased his life. But could his achievement have been possible without direct knowledge of Sisyphean struggle?

[7] Dante. *Inferno.* Trans. John Sinclair New York: Oxford University Press, 1972. (79)

CPSIA information can be obtained
at www.ICGtesting.com
Printed in the USA
LVHW101455050123
736439LV00003B/323